Central Course

These are the different types of pages and symbols used in this book:

This indicates the first page of a mathematical section.

7 Fractions and ratio: Calculations	These pages develop mathematical skills, concepts and facts in a wide variety of realistic contexts.

57 Extended context	Extended contexts require the use of skills from several different areas of mathematics in a section of work based on a single theme.

85 Detour: Ellipse	Detours provide self-contained activities which often require an exploratory, investigative approach, drawing on problem-solving skills.

29 Reasoning and application 1: Mixed problems	Reasoning and application pages contain a variety of problems set in different contexts which require the application of knowledge, skills and strategies previously learned.

Do Worksheet 1   This shows when you need to use a Worksheet.

● Remember   This is a reminder of the key information essential for the work of the pages.

▼ Challenge   Challenges are more demanding activities designed to stimulate further thought and discussion.

▮ Investigation   Investigations enhance the work of the page by providing additional opportunities to develop problem-solving skills.

Contents

At Camilla's Candies the cost in pence of each type of sweet is shown on the board.

The total cost of one special and one de-luxe selection is
$$4t + 2f + 5c + 6t + 3f + 8c$$
$$= 4t + 6t + 2f + 3f + 5c + 8c$$
$$= 10t + 5f + 13c$$

Five special selections cost
$$5(4t + 2f + 5c)$$
$$= 20t + 10f + 25c$$

Three special and four de-luxe selections cost
$$3(4t + 2f + 5c) + 4(6t + 3f + 8c)$$
$$= 12t + 6f + 15c + 24t + 12f + 32c$$
$$= 12t + 24t + 6f + 12f + 15c + 32c$$
$$= 36t + 18f + 47c$$

1 Find the cost in pence of these selections:

(a) 4 special

(b) 3 deluxe

(c) 2 special and 5 deluxe

(d) 7 special and 6 deluxe.

2 Simplify:

(a) $4x + 3x$

(b) $8m - 5m$

(c) $7y + y$

(d) $12s - s$

(e) $5r + 7r - 2r$

(f) $7d - 6d$

(g) $4a + 2b + 5a + 7b$

(h) $5p + 8q - 3p + 7q$

(i) $15w - 2z - 14w + 9z$

(j) $3m + 5n - m - 4n$

(k) $7r + 8s + 9t + 4r - 5s + 7t$

(l) $12a + 10b - 16c + a - 8b$

(m) $3v + 11 - v + 9$

(n) $2g - 12 + 8g + 7$

(o) $8k - 5j + 16 - 3k + 7j - 11$

3 Multiply:

(a) $4(3x + 2y)$

(b) $5(3a + b)$

(c) $7(4m - 5n)$

(d) $3(7g - 4h)$

(e) $10(f + 3g)$

(f) $2(2s - 6t)$

(g) $11(6f + 3g + 2)$

(h) $8(4a - 6b + 7)$

(i) $8(x - 5y - 4)$

(j) $3(5r + 7s + 3)$

4 Simplify:

(a) $2(3x + 5y) + 5(2x + 3y)$

(b) $4(5g + 2f) + 6(g + 3f)$

(c) $7(4r + 3s) + 5(2r - s)$

(d) $10(m - 6n) + 8(4m + n)$

(e) $7(6c + 6) + 3(2c - 9)$

(f) $5(9h + 5) + 8(4h + 3)$

(g) $3(3a + b + 2c) + 4(2a + 6b - c)$

(h) $6(6p - 7q + 10) + 5(3p + 6q - 12)$

(i) $5(2a + 7b - 6c + 8d) + 30c$

(j) $8(4d + 5e + 6) + 4d - 10e$

(k) $4(12r + 10s + 11t) + 3(r - 4s - 7t)$

(l) $9(2a + 6b - 3) + 7(5a - 5b)$

$7 \times 5 = 35$ so 7 and 5 are factors of 35
$5(2x + 7y) = 10x + 35y$ so 5 and $(2x + 7y)$ are factors of $10x + 35y$

Multiplying	Factorising
$3(3a + 5b)$	$9a + 15b$
$= 9a + 15b$	$= 3(3a + 5b)$

Multiplying	Factorising
$4(4p - q)$	$16p - 4q$
$= 16p - 4q$	$= 4(4p - q)$

To factorise $10x + 35y$

> 5 is a factor of $10x$ and
> 5 is a factor of $35y$.
> 5 is a **common factor** of
> $10x$ and $35y$.

so $10x + 35y = 5(2x + 7y)$

1 Factorise:

(a) $7m + 7n$ (b) $8f - 8g$ (c) $4c + 4d$
(d) $6r + 6s$ (e) $4t - 12$ (f) $6m + 24$

2 Factorise:

(a) $4m + 6n$ (b) $14r + 21s$ (c) $10p - 25q$
(d) $3j - 9k$ (e) $6t + 15$ (f) $7a + 49$
(g) $16h + 24j$ (h) $20x - 100$ (i) $18w - 81z$
(j) $12a + 4b + 10c$ (k) $14m - 28n + 35$
(l) $36p - 60q - 6$ (m) $15f + 33g - 27h$
(n) $22x - 55y + 121$ (o) $32d - 16e + 4$

To factorise $3p^2 + 6pq$

> $3p$ is a factor of $3p^2$
> and a factor of $6pq$

so $3p^2 + 6pq = 3p(p + 2q)$

$5x^2 - 10xy$
$= 5x(x - 2y)$

$16pq + 4q - 8qr$
$= 4q(4p + 1 - 2r)$

To factorise $x^2 + xy$

> x is a factor of x^2
> and a factor of xy

so $x^2 + xy = x(x + y)$

$a^2 - 3a + ac$
$= a(a - 3 + c)$

$3pq - 4p$
$= p(3q - 4)$

4 Factorise:

(a) $3x^2 + 9xy$ (b) $5y^2 - 15yz$
(c) $8r^2 + 12rs$ (d) $6ab + 9ac$
(e) $10mn + 25m^2$ (f) $7uv - 21uw$
(g) $24ac - 12bc$ (h) $15rs - 35rt$
(i) $16f^2 + 2fc$ (j) $9x^2 - 3xy + 15x$
(k) $12rs - 14rt - 10rw$ (l) $22fg + 33fh + 44f^2$
(m) $16jk + 32jmn$ (n) $30p^2 - 24pq + 18pr$
(o) $28abc - 21b^2d$

3 Factorise:

(a) $m^2 + 6m$ (b) $t^2 + 7t$ (c) $r^2 - 3r$
(d) $5s + st$ (e) $3g - fg$ (f) $de + dg$
(g) $3b^2 + 5b$ (h) $7m^2 - 6mn$ (i) $2w^2 - 7wz$
(j) $f^2 + 3fg - 6f$ (k) $r^2 - 2rs - 5rt$
(l) $m^2 - 5mn + 8mp$ (m) $x^2 + 9xy - 9x$
(n) $5dc + 4de + 7df$ (o) $3h^2 - 8hg - 9h$
(p) $3st - 5sp + 7s$ (q) $2a^2 + 4abc - ac$
(r) $3w^2 - 6wx + 7wxy$ (s) $8xz + 8xy - x$

5 Factorise:

(a) $7p - 14q$ (b) $12m + 8n$
(c) $25r + 15$ (d) $20a + 15b - 5c$
(e) $18u - 27v - 36w$ (f) $30p - 12q + 8$
(g) $45x + 55y + 35$ (h) $a^2 + 3a$
(i) $b^2 - 5b$ (j) $n^2 + 3mn$
(k) $pq + 7pr$ (l) $3f^2 - 5fg + 6f$
(m) $3d^2 - 6cd + 9d$ (n) $2rs + 4rp + 8r^2$
(o) $8xy + 12xw - 16xz$ (p) $15uv - 3u - 9u^2$
(q) $20abc + 10acd - 30abd$

Area of rectangle = length × breadth

$$= (4 + 6) \times (3 + 2)$$
$$= 4 \times 3 + 4 \times 2 + 6 \times 3 + 6 \times 2$$
$$= 12 + 8 + 18 + 12$$
$$= 50 \text{ units}^2$$

Check: $(4 + 6) \times (3 + 2)$
$$= 10 \times 5$$
$$= 50$$

We can use a diagram like this to multiply brackets.

$(5 + 3)(4 + 7) =$

$$= 20 + 35 + 12 + 21$$
$$= 88$$

1 Use a diagram to multiply these brackets.

(a) $(3 + 5)(2 + 7)$ **(b)** $(10 + 3)(4 + 6)$

(c) $(4 + 2)(7 + 5)$ **(d)** $(6 + 8)(9 + 4)$

To multiply brackets containing letters

$(x + 4)(x + 3) =$

$$= x^2 + 3x + 4x + 12$$
$$= x^2 + 7x + 12$$

2 Use a diagram to multiply these brackets.

(a) $(x + 2)(x + 5)$ **(b)** $(x + 8)(x + 7)$

(c) $(a + 8)(a + 3)$ **(d)** $(a + 6)(a + 5)$

(e) $(p + 11)(p + 8)$ **(f)** $(t + 8)(t + 1)$

(g) $(f + 4)(f + 12)$ **(h)** $(m + 10)(m + 10)$

(i) $(s + 3)(s + 11)$ **(j)** $(v + 4)(v + 16)$

$(x + 7)(x - 4) =$

$$= x^2 - 4x + 7x - 28$$
$$= x^2 + 3x - 28$$

3 Multiply these brackets.

(a) $(x + 7)(x - 2)$ **(b)** $(x + 4)(x - 1)$

(c) $(t + 3)(t - 2)$ **(d)** $(p + 7)(p - 5)$

(e) $(a + 5)(a - 9)$ **(f)** $(m + 11)(m - 6)$

(g) $(f - 3)(f + 8)$ **(h)** $(g - 12)(g + 6)$

(i) $(y - 10)(y + 11)$ **(j)** $(x - 6)(x + 5)$

(k) $(r - 5)(r + 5)$ **(l)** $(a + 9)(a - 9)$

(m) $(b + 3)(b - 3)$ **(n)** $(q - 10)(q + 1)$

$(x - 3)(x - 5) =$

negative × negative gives a positive

$$= x^2 - 5x - 3x + 15$$
$$= x^2 - 8x + 15$$

4 Multiply these brackets.

(a) $(x - 4)(x - 6)$ **(b)** $(y - 5)(y - 8)$

(c) $(p - 2)(p - 5)$ **(d)** $(t - 7)(t - 10)$

(e) $(a - 5)(a - 5)$ **(f)** $(m - 9)(m - 1)$

$(x + 4)(x + 3)$

$$= x(x + 3) + 4(x + 3)$$
$$= x \times x + x \times 3 + 4 \times x + 4 \times 3$$
$$= x^2 + 3x + 4x + 12$$
$$= x^2 + 7x + 12$$

5 Multiply these brackets.

(a) $(a + 5)(a + 11)$ **(b)** $(b + 9)(b + 7)$

(c) $(m + 6)(m + 6)$ **(d)** $(p + 10)(p + 2)$

(e) $(f + 5)(f - 4)$ **(f)** $(r - 4)(r + 7)$

(g) $(x - 3)(x - 4)$ **(h)** $(y - 7)(y - 10)$

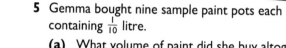

5 Gemma bought nine sample paint pots each containing $\frac{1}{10}$ litre.

    (a) What volume of paint did she buy altogether?

    (b) She used $\frac{2}{3}$ of the paint. What volume of paint did she use?

1 In Home World Frank bought 4 packets of nails each weighing $\frac{1}{5}$ kg.

    (a) What was the total weight of nails in kilograms bought by Frank?

    (b) Frank dropped half the nails. What weight of nails did he drop?

To find $\frac{1}{2}$ of $\frac{4}{5}$

$$\frac{1}{2} \text{ of } \frac{4}{5}$$

$$= \frac{1}{2} \times \frac{4}{5}$$

$$= \frac{1 \times 4}{2 \times 5}$$

$$= \frac{4}{10}$$

$$= \frac{2}{5}$$

To find $\frac{2}{3}$ of $\frac{9}{10}$

$$\frac{2}{3} \text{ of } \frac{9}{10}$$

$$= \frac{2}{3} \times \frac{9}{10}$$

$$= \frac{2 \times 9}{3 \times 10}$$

$$= \frac{18}{30}$$

$$= \frac{3}{5}$$

6 Calculate:

    (a) $\frac{2}{3}$ of $\frac{3}{5}$ **(b)** $\frac{3}{4}$ of $\frac{4}{15}$ **(c)** $\frac{2}{3}$ of $\frac{9}{10}$

    (d) $\frac{2}{5} \times \frac{5}{6}$ **(e)** $\frac{5}{6} \times \frac{6}{7}$ **(f)** $\frac{3}{5} \times \frac{5}{12}$

2 Calculate:

    (a) $\frac{1}{2}$ of $\frac{2}{3}$ **(b)** $\frac{1}{4}$ of $\frac{4}{5}$ **(c)** $\frac{1}{3}$ of $\frac{6}{7}$

    (d) $\frac{1}{2} \times \frac{4}{7}$ **(e)** $\frac{1}{5} \times \frac{5}{8}$ **(f)** $\frac{1}{4} \times \frac{8}{9}$

3 Frank had $\frac{9}{10}$ kg of wood screws. He used $\frac{1}{3}$ of them to build a table. What weight of screws did he use?

4 Frank's wife, Gemma, had $\frac{5}{12}$ litre of thinner in a bottle. She used $\frac{1}{5}$ of the thinner.

    What volume did she use?

7 Gemma bought five packets of paste each weighing $\frac{1}{8}$ kg.

    (a) What was the total weight of paste she bought?

    (b) Gemma used $\frac{3}{4}$ of the paste. What weight of paste did she use?

8 Frank has $\frac{3}{5}$ of a metre of plastic pipe. He used $\frac{3}{4}$ of this to connect his sink. What length of pipe did he use?

9 Gemma bought three-quarters of a metre of edging strip. She used two thirds of it.

    (a) What length did she use?

    (b) How much did she have left?

Home World

Frank has marked this strip of wood into tenths. The whole strip has ten pieces.

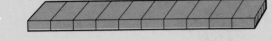

$1 \div \frac{1}{10}$

$= 1 \times \frac{10}{1}$

$= \frac{10}{1}$

$= 10$

Dividing by $\frac{1}{10}$ is the same as multiplying by 10.

1 Frank cuts a strip of wood into fifths. How many pieces does he get?
Copy and complete:

$1 \div \frac{1}{5}$

$= 1 \times \frac{5}{1}$

$= \boxed{}$

$= \boxed{}$

Dividing by $\frac{1}{5}$ is the same as $\boxed{}$.

2 Gemma cuts a strip of wood into eighths. How many pieces does she get?
Copy and complete the calculation.

$1 \div \frac{1}{8}$

$= 1 \times \frac{8}{1}$

$= \boxed{}$

$= \boxed{}$

Dividing by $\frac{1}{8}$ is the same as $\boxed{}$.

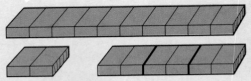

$\frac{1}{5}$ of the strip contains 2 pieces.

$\frac{1}{5} \div \frac{1}{10}$

$= \frac{1}{5} \times \frac{10}{1}$

$= \frac{1 \times 10}{5 \times 1}$

$= \frac{10}{5}$

$= 2$

$\frac{3}{5}$ of the strip contain 6 pieces.

$\frac{3}{5} \div \frac{1}{10}$

$= \frac{3}{5} \times \frac{10}{1}$

$= \frac{3 \times 10}{5 \times 1}$

$= \frac{30}{5}$

$= 6$

To find $\frac{5}{8} \div \frac{3}{4} = \frac{5}{8} \times \frac{4}{3}$

$= \frac{5 \times 4}{8 \times 3}$

$= \frac{20}{24}$

$= \frac{5}{6}$

Dividing by a fraction is the same as multiplying by the fraction 'upside-down'.

3 Calculate:

(a) $1 \div \frac{1}{4}$ (b) $3 \div \frac{1}{2}$ (c) $4 \div \frac{1}{3}$

(d) $\frac{2}{5} \div \frac{2}{3}$ (e) $\frac{2}{7} \div \frac{2}{3}$ (f) $\frac{5}{6} \div \frac{1}{3}$

(g) $\frac{3}{4} \div \frac{1}{8}$ (h) $\frac{9}{10} \div \frac{3}{5}$ (i) $\frac{8}{9} \div \frac{2}{3}$

4 How many pieces of wood each measuring $\frac{2}{3}$ of a metre can Gemma cut from a plank 4 metres long?

5 To make up paste Gemma needs 6 litres of water.

(a) How many times must she fill her $\frac{1}{2}$ litre jug to measure out 6 litres?

(b) How many times would she have to fill a jug of capacity $\frac{2}{5}$ of a litre?

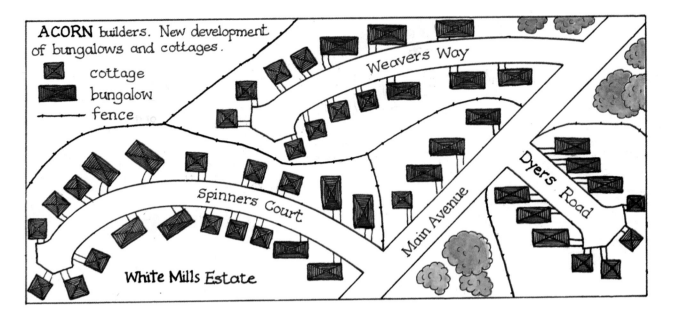

ACORN builders. New development of bungalows and cottages.

▨ cottage
▧ bungalow
⊢—⊢—⊢ fence

Weavers Way

Spinners Court

Main Avenue

Dyers Road

White Mills Estate

In Spinners Court there are
3 cottages to every 2 bungalows.

| The ratio of cottages to bungalows is | 3 to 2 |
| written as | 3 : 2 |

| The ratio of bungalows to cottages is | 2 to 3 |
| written as | 2 : 3. |

1 For each of the other streets write the ratio of:

   (a) cottages to bungalows

   (b) bungalows to cottages.

2 Each cottage has 4 windows at the front and 3 windows at the rear. Write the ratio of:

   (a) front windows to rear windows

   (b) rear windows to front windows.

3 Compost, made from coarse sand and peat, is added to each garden. For every 3 bags of coarse sand, 7 bags of peat are used. Write the ratio of:

   (a) coarse sand to peat

   (b) peat to coarse sand.

4 Luxury grass seed, a mixture of Fescue and Bent, is needed for the lawns. 5 bags of Fescue seed is mixed with 2 bags of Bent seed. Write the ratio of:

   (a) Fescue seed to Bent seed

   (b) Bent seed to Fescue seed.

In Spinners Court there are
12 cottages and 8 bungalows.

The ratio of cottages to bungalows is 12 : 8

The houses have been built in 4 equal groups.

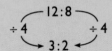

$$\begin{array}{c} \overset{\displaystyle 12:8}{} \\ \div 4 \qquad \div 4 \\ \overset{\displaystyle 3:2}{} \end{array}$$

The ratio 12 : 8 is **3 : 2 in simplest form**.

The ratio of cottages to bungalows is 3 : 2.

5 For Weavers Way write:

   (a) the number of cottages

   (b) the number of bungalows

   (c) the ratio of cottages to bungalows in simplest form.

6 Write each ratio in simplest form.

   (a) 4 : 8   **(b)** 10 : 4   **(c)** 6 : 9

   (d) 12 : 18   **(e)** 18 : 27   **(f)** 24 : 32

   (g) 25 : 35   **(h)** 36 : 30   **(i)** 45 : 27

   (j) 100 : 25   **(k)** 250 : 10   **(l)** 2000 : 4000

Concrete examples

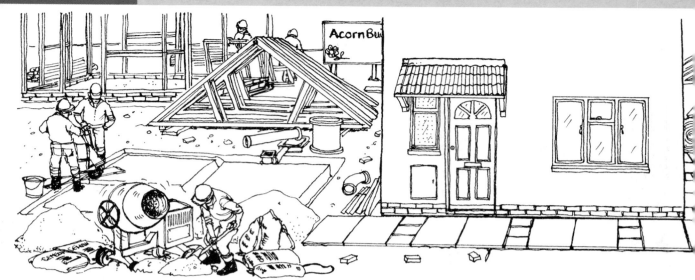

To make the concrete for the foundations, sand and cement are mixed in the ratio 5:2.
Dariusz has 40 bags of sand.
How many bags of cement should he use?

Sand	Cement
5	2
×8	×8
40	16

He should use **16 bags of cement**.

1 For concrete, how many bags of cement should Dariusz use if he has these bags of sand?

   (a) 20   (b) 35   (c) 50   (d) 75

2 How many bags of sand should he use if he has these bags of cement?

   (a) 8   (b) 12   (c) 20   (d) 34

3 Cement and sand can be mixed in the ratio 1:9 to make mortar. How much sand is needed when the number of bags of cement is:

   (a) 10   (b) 16   (c) 22   (d) 5?

4 Red slabs and white slabs, in the ratio 2:3, are to be laid for pathways. How many white slabs are needed when the number of red slabs used is:

   (a) 10   (b) 24   (c) 36   (d) 44?

5 Timber frames are used in the construction of the houses. The ratio of roof frames to wall frames is 7:4. How many roof frames are needed when the number of wall frames used is:

   (a) 20   (b) 28   (c) 40   (d) 48?

6 For each villa, bricks and breeze blocks are used in the ratio 60:40.

   (a) Write this ratio in simplest form.

   (b) Calculate the number of breeze blocks needed when the number of bricks is:

   • 1200   • 1500   • 1830   • 2130

7 Jackie is improving each garden by adding a mixture of topsoil and compost in the ratio 7:3. How many bags of topsoil will she need when the number of bags of compost is:

   (a) 21   (b) 27   (c) 42   (d) 48?

Ken is mixing sand and cement in the ratio 7:3 to make mortar.
7 m^3 of sand and 3 m^3 of cement would make 10 m^3 of mortar mix.
How much of each is needed for a total of 30 m^3 of mortar mix?

Total	Sand	Cement
10	7	3
×3	×3	×3
30	21	9

21 m^3 **of sand** and 9 m^3 **of cement** are needed.

8 How much sand and how much cement does Ken use if the amount of mortar mix he made was:
(a) 40 m^3 (b) 60 m^3 (c) 80 m^3 (d) 100 m^3?

9 For stronger mortar, he mixes sand and cement in the ratio 3:5. How much of each does he need for the following quantities of mortar?
(a) 24 m^3 (b) 56 m^3 (c) 72 m^3 (d) 88 m^3

10 Jackie is sowing the lawn of each cottage with Fescue and Bent seed in the ratio 2:3. What weight of each seed would she require for the following weights of the mixture?
(a) 40 kg (b) 60 kg (c) 35 kg (d) 75 kg

11 Louise has delivered twenty five cubic metres of gravel. The ratio of white gravel to red gravel in this delivery is 2:9.
Calculate the volume of each colour of gravel, correct to 1 decimal place.

12 Paint and white spirit are mixed in the ratio 2:1 to make undercoat. If 40 litres of undercoat are needed, calculate the volume of paint and of white spirit required, correct to 1 decimal place.

13 Myra and John, the two company directors, used to share profits in the ratio 3:4. How much did each receive when the total profit was:
(a) £21 000 (b) £56 000 (c) £1·4 million?

14 Myra has increased her shares in Acorn Builders. Myra and John now share profits in the ratio 5:4. How much will each receive now if the total profit is:
(a) £26 100 (b) £57 600 (c) £1·8 million?

▶ **Challenge**

15 Sand, gravel and cement are mixed in the ratio 5:2:1 to make concrete.
How much of each is needed for 32 m^3 of concrete?

You need $\frac{1}{2}$ cm squared and isometric paper.

1 Follow these instructions to create a design based on squares.
- Select four pencils, each a different colour, and number the colours ①, ②, ③, and ④.
- Shade a square in the centre of the sheet using colour ①.
- Use colour ② to shade **every** square which touches the first coloured square along **one** side only.
- Use colour ③ to shade every square which touches the second coloured squares along one side only.
- Use colour ④ to shade every square which touches the third coloured squares along one side only.
- Continue in this way, going back to colour ① after colour ④.

2 Use isometric paper to create a similar design based on triangles.

Packham's plc make containers in the shape of prisms.

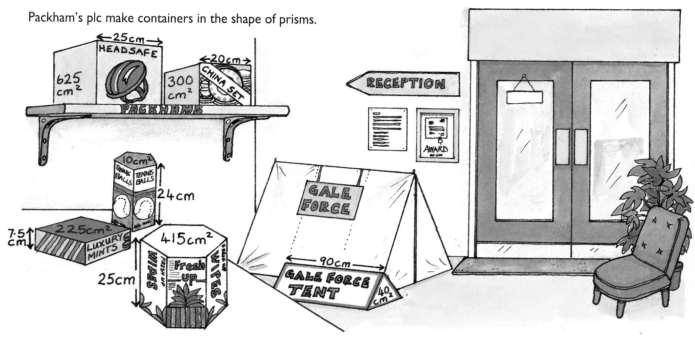

1 Copy and complete the table for the 6 containers above.

Product name	Prism
Head Safe Cycle Helmet	Cube
Gale Force Tent	

● **Remember**

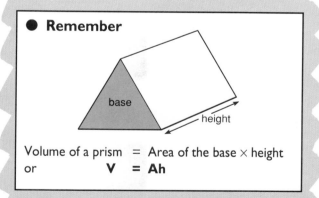

Volume of a prism = Area of the base × height

or **V = Ah**

To find the volume of the *Gale Force* box:

Volume of *Gale Force* box = 40 × 90

= 3600 cm³

The volume of the *Gale Force* box is 3600 cm³.

2 Find the volume of each of the other containers.

3 Find the volume of:

(a) the hut (b) the skip

(c) the van's storage space (d) the grit bin.

4 ▶ Do Worksheet 1.

5 Shapes S and T on Worksheet 1 are drawn on 1 cm dot paper. Find the volume of each shape.

The Daisy Chain

The Daisy Chain, a company producing cream cheese, makes presentation packs. Ramsay has to find the volume of each cylindrical pack.

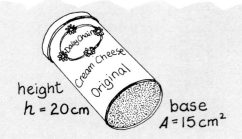

height
$h = 20$ cm

base
$A = 15$ cm²

A cylinder is a prism with a circular base.

Volume of the cylinder $= Ah$
$$V = 15 \times 20$$
$$V = 300 \text{ cm}^3$$
The volume of the cylinder is **300 cm³**.

1 Find the volume of each cylindrical pack.

(a)
$A = 35$ cm²

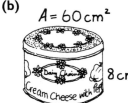
12 cm

(b)
$A = 60$ cm²

8 cm

(c)
$A = 45$ cm²

13 cm

(d)
$A = 36$ cm²

18 cm

(e)
$A = 125$ cm²

5 cm

(f)
$A = 65$ cm²

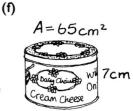
7 cm

2 Find the volume of each half cylinder.

(a)

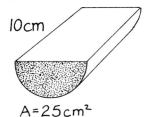
10 cm
$A = 25$ cm²

(b)

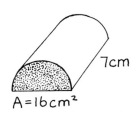
7 cm
$A = 16$ cm²

3 (a) Find the volume of this cylinder.

(b) Ramsay wants to pack 24 of these cylinders into the cardboard box. Find the inside dimensions of the box if each cylinder has a diameter of 8 cm.

(c) Find the volume of the box.

(d) Find the total volume of the 24 cylinders.

(e) Find the difference between the volume of the box and the volume of the 24 cylinders.

$A = 50$ cm²

12 cm

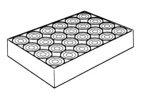

■ **Investigation**

4 Design other boxes to hold the 24 cylinders. In each case find the difference between the volume of the boxes and the total volume of the cylinders.

● Remember

The area of a circle is
found using the formula
$A = \pi r^2$
where A is the area and
r is the radius.

6 cm

$A = \pi r^2$
$A = 3 \cdot 14 \times 6 \times 6$
$A = 113 \cdot 04$
The area is **113 cm²** to the nearest square
centimetre.

The value of π is 3·14, correct to 3 significant
figures.
Answers should also be given to this accuracy.
113·04 = 113 to 3 significant figures
3728·2 = 3730 to 3 significant figures.

5 Find the area of each of these cheese labels.

(a)
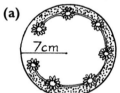
7cm

(b)

2 cm

6 Find the area of a circular label of:
   (a) radius 8·3 cm   **(b)** diameter 17 cm.

For a cylinder
$V = Ah$

The base is a circle, so
A is πr^2.

The volume, V, is therefore
$V = \pi r^2 h$.

$V = \pi r^2 h$
$V = 3 \cdot 14 \times 4 \times 4 \times 9$
$V = 452 \cdot 16$

The volume of the cylinder is **452 cm³**
to the nearest cubic centimetre.

7 Find the volume of each cylinder correct to the
nearest cm³.

(a)
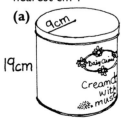
9cm
19cm
Cream
with
mus

(b)
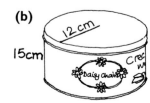
12 cm
15cm
Cream
wi

8 Find the volume of each cylinder correct to
   3 significant figures.

(a)
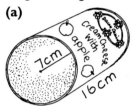
7cm
16cm

(b)

3cm
11cm

(c)
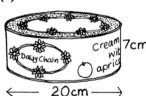
Cream
wil
apric
7cm
Daisy Chain
← 20cm →

(d)
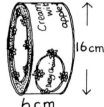
16cm
6 cm

9 Ramsay makes a cylindrical display pack with radius
   27 cm and length 90 cm. Calculate its volume.

10 Cream cheese is prepared in a cylindrical vat with
   diameter 120 cm and height 150 cm. Find the
   volume of the vat in:
   (a) cubic centimetres   **(b)** litres.

11 These presentation packs are in the shape of half
   cylinders. Find the volume of each.

(a)
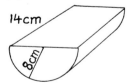
14cm
8cm

(b)
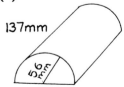
137mm
56 mm

■ Investigation

12 Ramsay wants to double the volume of a cylinder.
   Should he double the radius or double the height?

Prism Play Centre

Brenda is designing shapes for the soft play area in the Prism Play Centre. All her designs are prisms. For each shape she has to calculate the volume of foam needed.

The base of this prism is a right-angled triangle.

Area of triangle
$A = \frac{1}{2}bh$
$A = \frac{1}{2} \times 30 \times 40$
$A = 600 \text{ cm}^2$.

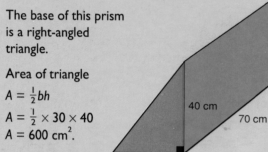

Volume of prism
$V = Ah$
$V = 600 \times 70$
$V = 42\,000 \text{ cm}^3$
Brenda needs **42 000 cm³** or **42 litres** of foam.

1 Find the volume of foam needed for each shape.
Give each answer in:
• cubic centimetres • litres.

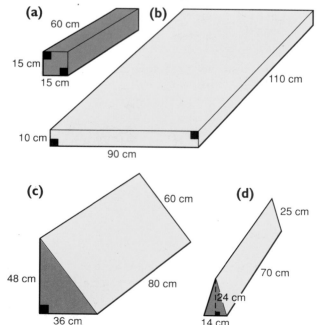

(a)

60 cm
15 cm
15 cm

(b)

110 cm
10 cm
90 cm

(c)

60 cm
48 cm
80 cm
36 cm

(d)

25 cm
70 cm
24 cm
14 cm

Brenda also needs to calculate the surface area to find the amount of material needed to cover each shape.

This is another view of Brenda's design.

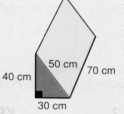

50 cm
40 cm
70 cm
30 cm

Two faces are right-angled triangles.

Area of a triangle $= \frac{1}{2} \times 30 \times 40$
$= 600 \text{ cm}^2$
Area of 2 triangles $= 1200 \text{ cm}^2$

40 cm
30 cm
30 cm

The other 3 faces are rectangles.

Area $= 50 \times 70$
$= 3500 \text{ cm}^2$

50 cm
70 cm

Area $= 40 \times 70$
$= 2800 \text{ cm}^2$

40 cm
70 cm

Area $= 30 \times 70$
$= 2100 \text{ cm}^2$

30 cm
70 cm

Total surface area is
$1200 + 3500 + 2800 + 2100 = 9600 \text{ cm}^2$
Brenda will need **9600 cm²** of material.

2 Calculate the total surface area for each of Brenda's designs in question 1.

3 ▶ Do Worksheet 2.

Brenda is making a cylinder for the soft play area.
The cover will be made from 2 circles and a rectangle.

Circumference of the circle = πd
$= 3{\cdot}14 \times 60$
$= 188{\cdot}4$
The length of the rectangle is **188 cm**.

$d = 2r$
$d = 60$ cm

Area of the rectangle
$A = lb$
$A = 188 \times 80 = 15\,040$
The area of the rectangle is **15 000 cm²**.

Area of the circle
$C = \pi r^2$
$C = 3{\cdot}14 \times 30 \times 30 = 2826$
The area of each circle is **2830 cm²**.

Total surface area = area of circles + area of rectangle
$= 2830 + 2830 + 15\,000$
$= 20\,660$ cm²
The total surface area is **20 700 cm²** (to 3 sig figs).

30 cm
80 cm

30 cm
188 cm
80 cm
30 cm

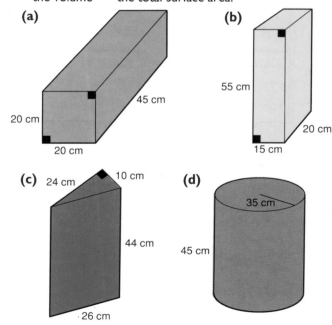

4 For each cylinder find:
 • the circumference of the circle
 • the total surface area.

(a)

25 cm
50 cm

(b)

10 cm
70 cm

(c)

60 cm
18 cm

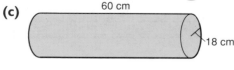

(d)

50 cm
20 cm

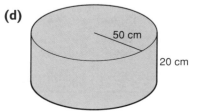

5 For each soft play shape find:
 • the volume • the total surface area.

(a)

20 cm
20 cm
45 cm

(b)

55 cm
20 cm
15 cm

(c) 24 cm
10 cm
44 cm
26 cm

(d)

35 cm
45 cm

▸ Challenge

6 A cube has a surface area of 5400 cm². What is the
length of a side?

Card calculators

1 Copy and complete the table to show how all the whole numbers between 1 and 15 can be made by adding the figures 1, 2, 4 and 8 only. Each figure can be used only once.

For example $7 = 1 + 2 + 4$

Number	1	2	4	8
1				
2				
3				
4				
5				
6				
7	✓	✓	✓	
8				
9				

2 Here are 4 card calculators.

Card A
1	3	5	7
9	11	13	15

Card B
2	3	6	7
10	11	14	15

Card C
4	5	6	7
12	13	14	15

Card D
8	9	10	11
12	13	14	15

(a) Choose a whole number between 1 and 15.
(b) List the cards on which your number appears.
(c) Write the first number from each of these cards.
(d) Add these numbers.
(e) What do you notice?

3 Repeat question 2 for different numbers.

4 Look at your table from question 1. Compare it with the calculator cards. How do you decide on which card or cards a number should appear?

5 Five calculator cards are needed to make numbers up to 31.

Card A
1	3	5	7
9	11	13	15
17	19	21	23
25	27	29	31

Card B
2	3	6	7
10	11	14	15
18	19	22	23
26	27	30	31

Card C
4	5	6	7
12	13	14	15
20	21	22	23
28	29	30	31

Card D
8	9	10	11
12	13	14	15
24	25	26	27
28	29	30	31

(a) **Card E** begins with the number 16. Draw and complete **Card E**.
(b) Test your card for three numbers between 1 and 31.

▼ Challenge

6 Six calculator cards are needed to make numbers up to 63. Two of the cards are shown below.
(a) Complete the set.
(b) Test your cards for three numbers between 1 and 63.

Card A
1	3	5	7	9	11	13	15
17	19	21	23	25	27	29	31
33	35	37	39	41	43	45	47
49	51	53	55	57	59	61	63

Card D
8	9	10	11	12	13	14	15
24	25	26	27	28	29	30	31
48	49	50	51	52	53	54	55
56	57	58	59	60	61	62	63

Laura and Ashraf are job hunting.
These two advertisements from the local paper
interest them. Which job is better paid?

SALESPERSON REQUIRED

for busy city centre store.

**$37\frac{1}{2}$ hour week.
Wage £120**

No previous experience necessary but must be enthusiastic and hard working.

Apply in writing to:
**The Manager, Patches,
37 High Street.**

YOUNG PERSON

wanted as
trainee receptionist
in busy dental practice.

Must have a pleasant manner.
40 hour week.
Salary £546 per month

Apply in writing to:
M Olar, Dental Practice,
63 Canine Lane.

What are the annual earnings for each job?

Weekly wage = £120	Monthly salary = £546
Annual earnings = £120 × 52 = **£6240**	Annual earnings = £546 × 12 = **£6552**

The **receptionist's job** has the greater annual earnings.

What is the hourly rate of pay for each job?

Weekly wage = £120
Hourly rate = £120 ÷ 37·5 = **£3·20**

Annual earnings = £6552
Weekly earnings = £6552 ÷ 52 = £126
Hourly rate = £126 ÷ 40 = **£3·15**

The **salesperson's job** has the greater hourly rate of pay.

Although the receptionist's job has the greater annual earnings, the salesperson's job has the greater hourly rate.

---

1 Brian is paid a weekly wage of £128. Calculate his annual earnings.

2 Sandra is paid a monthly salary of £725. How much is she paid per annum?

3 Liam is paid a weekly wage of £186. How much is this: **(a)** per annum
(b) per calendar month?

4 Syeda earns £760 per month.
Elias earns £170 per week.
Who has the greater annual earnings?

5 Sally earns a salary of £825 per month, Des earns a weekly wage of £192 and Shabana is paid £10 000 per year. Who has the greatest annual earnings?

6 Samantha is paid £3·10 per hour. How much will she earn for working 40 hours?

7 Frank earns £3·56 per hour. How much will he earn for working $37\frac{1}{2}$ hours?

8 Omar's rate of pay is £4·60 per hour and he works $32\frac{1}{2}$ hours each week. Sabrina's rate of pay is £4·45 per hour and she works 37 hours each week. Who earns the most each week?

9 Sarah earns £124·20 for working 36 hours. What is her hourly rate?

10 Dave earns £140·80 for working a 40 hour week. Pam earns £134·90 for working a 38 hour week. Who has the better hourly rate of pay?

Ashraf successfully applied for the receptionist's job. At the end of his first month he expected to receive £546. In fact he only received £404. This is his pay slip.

Name	Reference	Pay to	Tax Code	NI Number
A Bashire	R 004	31/10/95	350L	RT 654392 B
Basic Pay	**Overtime**	**Bonus**	**Additional Payment**	**Gross Pay**
£546·00	£0·00	£0·00	£40·00	£586·00
Nat. Insurance	**Income Tax**	**Pension**	**Other**	**Total Deductions**
£52·74	£73·08	£56·18	£0·00	£182·00
				Net Pay
				£404·00

Use Ashraf's pay slip.

1 For which month did he receive this salary?

2 Reference numbers are used for all employees in firms or businesses. Write Ashraf's reference number.

3 Income tax is paid to the Government. Each employee has a tax code which is used to calculate the amount of income tax to be paid.
(a) What is Ashraf's tax code?
(b) How much did he pay in income tax?

4 NI stands for National Insurance. This money is used to fund the Health Service, state pensions, sick pay, unemployment benefit and other payments.
(a) What is Ashraf's National Insurance number?
(b) How much did he pay in National Insurance?

5 How much did Ashraf pay towards his pension?

6 National Insurance, income tax and pension payments are added together to give Ashraf's **total deductions**. Write his total deductions.

7 What was Ashraf's basic pay?

8 Ashraf was given an additional payment to help him buy clothes for his new job. How much was his additional payment?

9 Ashraf's basic pay and additional payment give his **gross pay**. How much was his gross pay?

10 Ashraf's **net pay** is the amount he takes home every month. It is found by subtracting his total deductions from his gross salary. What was Ashraf's net pay?

Gross Pay = Basic Pay + Bonus + Additional Payments
Total Deductions = NI + Income Tax + Pension + Other Deductions
Net Pay = Gross Pay – Total Deductions

11 ▶ **Do Worksheet 3.**

When you start work you can expect to have about $\frac{1}{3}$ of your earnings deducted.

Jenny is a trainee chef earning £130 per week. **Estimate** her net pay.
$\frac{1}{3}$ of £130 = £43 to the nearest £.
£130 – £43 = £87
She can expect to take home about **£87** each week.

12 **Estimate** the net pay for each of the following.
(a) Paul is a printer earning £140 per week.
(b) Mary is an apprentice plumber who earns £148 per week.
(c) Pamela is a van driver earning £128 per week.
(d) Jackie is a technician earning £725 per month.
(e) Shamsad is a trainee manager earning £680 per month.

■ **Investigation**

13 Look at job adverts in your local paper. Choose jobs in which you are interested and **estimate** the net pay.

For many jobs the **basic working week** is between 35 hours and 40 hours. Additional hours worked is called **overtime**.

Heather is a welder who works a basic **38 hour week**. She is paid at the rate of £4·60 per hour. Overtime is paid at **time and a half**.
Find her pay for working 45 hours in one week.

Basic pay = £4·60 × 38 = **£174·80**

Overtime = 45 – 38 = 7 hours

Time and a half means that for each hour of overtime she is paid for $1\frac{1}{2}$ hours.

Hours to be paid = 7 hours × $1\frac{1}{2}$ = $10\frac{1}{2}$ hours

Overtime pay   = £4·60 × $10\frac{1}{2}$ = **£48·30**

Gross pay = Basic pay + Overtime
      = £174·80 + £48·30
      = **£223·10**

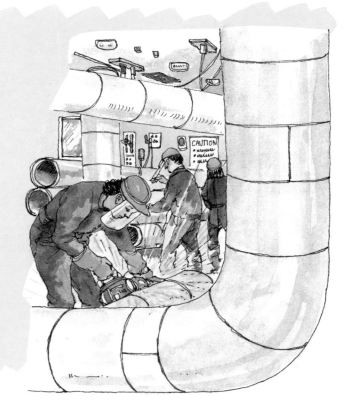

1   Sheila is a computer operator. She works a basic 35 hour week and is paid £3·60 per hour. Overtime is paid at time and a half. If she worked 40 hours in one week find:
   (a) her basic pay
   (b) her overtime pay
   (c) her gross pay.

2   Ashley is a secretary who works a basic $37\frac{1}{2}$ hour week and is paid £3·36 per hour. Overtime is paid at time and a half. Find his gross pay for a week in which he worked 44 hours.

Hours to be paid at:
time and a quarter = overtime × $1\frac{1}{4}$

time and a third   = overtime × $1\frac{1}{3}$

time and a half   = overtime × $1\frac{1}{2}$
double time   = overtime × 2.

---

3   Ross is a nanny who looks after two young children. He works a basic 38 hour week and is paid £3·36 per hour. At weekends he is paid double time. Calculate his gross pay if he worked his basic week, plus 4 hours on Saturday and 2 hours on Sunday.

4   Diane is a plumber who is paid £4·08 per hour for a basic 32 hour week. Overtime is paid at time and a quarter. Calculate Diane's gross pay for a week in which she worked 39 hours.

5   At weekends Mark is paid time and a half. His basic hourly rate is £3·86 for a $37\frac{1}{2}$ hour week. One week he worked 7 hours overtime at the weekend. Calculate his gross pay.

6   Pierre is a chef who works a basic 39 hour week at the hourly rate of £5·64. Overtime is paid at time and a third. Find his gross pay for a week in which he worked 48 hours.

7   Shelly is a receptionist who is paid an hourly rate of £4·16 for a basic 35 hour week. Overtime rates are time and a half for weekdays and double time at weekends. One week she worked her basic week and the following overtime: Monday 3 hours, Wednesday 2 hours, Friday 1 hour, Sunday 4 hours. Calculate her gross pay.

On time

Laura successfully applied for the job at Patches. Her time card, with which she clocks in and out, is used to record the hours worked. This is her time card for her second week.

Name L Thomson			Week beginning 5 October		
Day	In	Out	In	Out	Hours worked
Mon	08.30	12.00	13.00	17.00	7.5
Tue	08.30	12.00	13.00	19.00	9.5
Wed			13.00	17.00	4.0
Thu	08.28	12.00			3.5
Fri	08.29	12.01	12.58	17.00	7.5
Sat	08.30	12.02	13.00	17.01	7.5
Sun					

1 At what time do you think Laura:
  (a) starts work in the morning
  (b) starts her lunch break
  (c) normally finishes for the day?

2 Laura does not get paid overtime for working on Saturdays but is given time off during the week.
  (a) Which morning is she given off?
  (b) Which afternoon is she given off?

3 Find the total number of hours Laura worked.

4 Laura is paid £3·20 per hour for a basic $37\frac{1}{2}$ hour week. Overtime is paid at time and a half. Calculate her gross pay for this week.

5 Paul also works at Patches and is paid the same rates as Laura. This is his time card. Calculate his gross pay.

Name P Bentley			Week beginning 5 October		
Day	In	Out	In	Out	Hours worked
Mon	09.00	12.30	13.30	17.30	7.5
Tue	09.00	12.30	13.30	19.30	9.5
Wed					
Thu	08.28	12.00	13.00	17.31	8.0
Fri	09.00	12.30	13.30	17.32	7.5
Sat	08.58	12.30	13.00	17.30	8.0
Sun					

6 ▶ **Do Worksheet 4.**

Lucy and Sean sell clothes to Patches and other shops. They are paid a percentage of the value of their total sales each week. This is called **commission**. Their rate of commission is $2\frac{1}{2}$%.

In the week beginning 5 October Lucy sold £4260 worth of clothes.
Commission = $2\frac{1}{2}$% of £4260 = £106·50

7 In the same week Sean sold £3928 worth of clothes. Calculate his commission.

8 Mrs Kay works for a mail order company. She receives no basic wage but earns $8\frac{1}{4}$% commission on all her sales. How much will she earn if her sales total £844?

9 Sabrina is a manager at Pinstripes. She receives 4% commission on weekly sales above £2000. How much will she earn in commission if the weekly sales total £3624?

10 Angus sells double glazing and earns $6\frac{3}{4}$% commission on monthly sales over £5000. Calculate his commission in a month when his sales are worth £9340.

11 Dave sells fitted kitchens and is paid commission on all sales. One week he sold £10 670 worth of kitchens and earned £426·80. What is his rate of commission?

National Insurance is paid by both the employee and employer.

Employees pay about 9% of their gross pay in National Insurance.

Last week Laura's gross pay was £146·60.
NI contribution = 9% of £146·60
           = £13·19
Laura paid **£13·19** in National Insurance.

1 Find the National Insurance contribution for each employee.
   (a) Senga works in a food factory. Her gross pay last week was £184.
   (b) Barry is a mechanic. His gross pay last week was £206.
   (c) Ihab is a lab technician. Last month his gross salary was £1284.
   (d) Mairi is a dental technician. Last month her gross salary was £1495.

When people reach retirement age they receive a state pension. Many employers arrange an additional pension scheme. This is often called **superannuation**. Employees contribute about 5% of their gross pay to a superannuation fund.

Fara earns £1356 per month. She contributes 5% of her gross salary towards her superannuation.
How much does she pay?
Superannuation = 5% of £1356 = £67·80
She pays **£67·80** each month.

2 Ramsay earns £184 per week. He contributes $4\frac{1}{4}$% of his gross wage towards superannuation. How much does he pay each week?

3 Rebecca is an electrician and earns £324 per week. She pays $5\frac{1}{2}$% of her gross pay for superannuation. How much does she pay each week?

Income tax is deducted by the Government to fund, for example, defence, national and local government and public services. Everyone is allowed to earn a certain amount of money before paying tax. This **allowance** depends on individual circumstances. The first 3 figures of the allowance are used in the tax code. Earnings which exceed the allowance are called **taxable income**.

Linda earns £1425 per month.
Her allowance is £3442 per annum.
What is her: • tax code number
             • taxable income?

Tax code number **344**
Annual income   = £1425 × 12 = £17 100
Taxable income = Annual gross pay – Allowance
          = £17 100 – £3442
          = **£13 658**

4 Matthew earns £1542 per month. His allowance is £4247. Calculate his taxable income.

5 Sally earns £169·50 per week. Her allowance is £5227. Calculate her taxable income.

The amount of income tax to be paid is calculated from taxable income. Rates in use are:
   20% on the first £2500 of taxable income
   25% on the next £21 200 of taxable income
   40% on taxable income over £23 700.

Linda's taxable income is £13 658.
Linda's income tax is
20% of £2500   = £500·00
25% of (£13 658 – £2500)   = £2789·50
Total income tax = £500·00 + £2789·50 = **£3289·50**

6 Iestyn has a part-time job as a librarian and earns £475 per month. His allowance is £3445. Calculate his:
   (a) annual salary   **(b)** taxable income
   (c) annual income tax.

7 Francis earns £138 per week. His allowance is £3749. Find his: **(a)** annual income   **(b)** taxable income
                (c) annual income tax.

8 Petra earns £1645 per month. Her allowance is £6388. Calculate her **monthly** income tax.

1

RECEPTIONIST
required for busy Opticians

$37\frac{1}{2}$ **hour week, £4·20 per hour.**
Flexible working hours.
Must be smart and confident.
No previous experience necessary.
Apply Lenzies, High St.

(a) Write the hourly rate of pay for a receptionist at Lenzies.
(b) Calculate the basic weekly wage.

2 Grant is a painter and decorator. His basic wage is £165 per week. His employers give him a 5% wage rise. What is his new weekly wage?

3 Sajid works a basic $37\frac{1}{2}$ hour week and is paid £165·75. What is his hourly rate?

4 Linda sells fitted kitchens. She earns a salary of £800 per month plus $2\frac{1}{2}$% commission on all sales. Last month her sales totalled £25 680. Calculate her gross monthly salary.

5 Kirsty works in a shop and is paid £3·24 per hour for a basic 35 hour week. Overtime is paid at time and a half.
(a) Calculate her gross wage for a week in which she works 12 hours overtime.
(b) In the same week she pays £13·45 National Insurance, £9·64 superannuation and £28·87 income tax. Find her net pay.

6 Rhona works for a mail order company. She earns 5% commission on the first £1000 of her sales and $7\frac{1}{2}$% on sales over £1000. Calculate her gross salary when her sales are:
(a) £856   (b) £1328   (c) £2548.

7 Unah earns £1775 per month. Her tax allowance is £6453 per annum. Income tax rates are
20% on the first £2500 of taxable income
25% on the next £21 200 of taxable income
40% on taxable income over £23 700.
Find her:
(a) annual salary
(b) taxable income
(c) annual income tax.

8 Dermot earns £1885 per month driving Le Shuttle. He pays 6·4% in National Insurance and 5·8% on a pension scheme.
Calculate his monthly:
(a) National Insurance contribution
(b) pension contribution.

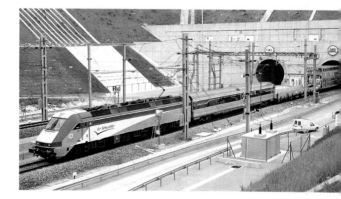

9 Andy Pane sells double and triple glazing. He earns £70 per week plus 4% commission on all double glazing sales and $6\frac{3}{4}$% commission on all triple glazing sales. Last week he sold £1690 worth of double glazing and £1448 worth of triple glazing. Calculate his gross wage for last week.

10 Paul builds wooden fences. He is paid £1·25 per metre for the first 200 metres and £1·50 per metre for each additional metre built. Calculate his gross pay when he builds 245 metres of fencing.

11 Sandra works part-time at home addressing envelopes. She earns £8·65 for every 100 she addresses. Calculate her gross pay for this week.

Day	Number of envelopes addressed
Mon	349
Tue	217
Wed	325
Thu	0
Fri	0
Sat	172
Sun	237

Laura has bought a car and needs to insure it. The cost of insurance depends on many factors, including the driver's age and experience, the type of car, the type of insurance and the district where the car is based.

The table shows the annual comprehensive **premium** for different car groups and districts.

Safeguard Insurance Company

Category	Insurance group					
	1	2	3	4	5	6
A	£480	£556	£676	£800	£946	£1090
B	£524	£610	£738	£872	£1032	£1192
C	£564	£708	£792	£938	£1110	£1278
D	£608	£748	£856	£1012	£1198	£1388
E	£664	£770	£932	£1102	£1304	£1502
F	£722	£840	£1016	£1202	£1424	£1640

Young drivers pay an additional percentage based on their age and experience.

Laura has bought a Ford Escort 1·3L, which is a group 3 car. She lives in Edinburgh, which is in category D. As she is only 18 years old she will pay an additional 50%.

Basic premium = £856
Age payment = 50% of £856 = £428
Total premium = £856 + £428 = **£1284**

1 Paul is 20 years old and has a Metro 1·3 LE, which is in insurance group 2. He pays an additional 50% because of his age. He lives in Yorkshire, which is in category B. Calculate his annual insurance premium.

2 Fiona is 42 years old and owns a Nissan 1·6 GL, which is in group 5. She lives in the West End of Glasgow, which is in category E. Calculate her annual insurance premium.

3 Sheila is 24 years old and owns a Renault 5 GTL, which is in group 3. She lives in Nottingham, which is in category B. As a young driver, she pays an additional 10%. How much is her annual premium?

A **no claims bonus** is a discount given to drivers who do not make a claim on their insurance. The amount depends on the number of years without a claim.

Number of years without a claim	1	2	3	4 or more
No claims bonus	30%	40%	50%	60%

If you claim on your insurance you lose all or part of your bonus.

Harry is 38 and lives in the Lake District, which is in category B. He has been driving for 2 years and has not claimed on his insurance. He owns a Maestro 1·6 HL, which is in group 4. How much will it cost him to insure his car?

Basic premium = £872
No claims bonus = 40%
Discount = 40% of £872 = £348·80
Premium = £872 − £348·80 = £523·20.
His insurance will cost **£523·20**.

4 Sami has a Ford Escort 1·6 L, which is in group 4. She is an experienced driver and has not made a claim in the last 2 years. She lives in Rhyl, which is in category C. How much is her annual premium?

5 Ihab drives a Saab 900i, which is in group 6. He has a maximum no claims bonus and lives in Oxford, which is in category D. How much will it cost him to insure his car?

6 The Safeguard Insurance Company has announced a 6% increase in all premiums. Bill has a Vauxhall Cavalier 2·0i, which is in group 6. He lives in the centre of Birmingham, which is in category F. He has not made an insurance claim in the last year.

(a) How much would it have cost him to insure his car before the price rise?

(b) How much will it cost him now?

■ Investigation

7 There are two main types of car insurance:
• comprehensive
• third party, fire and theft.
Investigate each type of policy.

Planning for the future

Ashraf has decided to find out about **assurance** policies. Sheena, a financial adviser gives him information.

She also gives Ashraf a table for calculating monthly premiums for one life assurance company.

There are two main types of assurance
• whole life
• endowment.
Premiums for a whole life policy are paid as long as the insured person is alive. The sum assured is paid when the person dies.
Premiums for an endowment policy are paid for an agreed length of time. The sum assured is paid at the end of the term or on death.

Surenough Life Assurance										
Monthly premiums for every £1000 assured										
Age next birthday		20	21	22	23	24	25	26	27	28
Whole life		£1·95	£1·95	£2·00	£2·05	£2·05	£2·10	£2·12	£2·15	£2·18
Endowment term	15 years	£7·65	£7·80	£8·00	£8·25	£8·40	£8·55	£8·60	£8·80	£9·05
	20 years	£5·55	£5·60	£5·80	£6·00	£7·25	£7·50	£7·75	£8·00	£8·30
	25 years	£4·10	£4·20	£4·35	£4·40	£4·60	£4·85	£5·10	£5·35	£5·65

Whole life

Ashraf will be 20 next birthday. He wants a whole life policy for £8000.

Sum assured	Monthly premium
£1000	£1·95
£8000	£1·95 × 8 = £15·60

His whole life policy will cost **£15·60** per month.

Endowment

He also wants an endowment policy over 20 years for £6200.

Sum assured	Monthly premium
£1000	£5·55
£6200	£5·55 × 6·2 = £34·41

His endowment policy will cost **£34·41** per month.

1 Robin will be 25 next birthday. What would be his monthly premium for a whole life policy for:
   (a) £1000   (b) £6000?

2 Sandra will be 28 next birthday. She wants to take out an endowment policy over 25 years for £8000. What will be her monthly premium?

3 Ian is 24 years old. He wants to take out a whole life policy for £4500. How much will he have to pay each month?

4 Shabina is 27 years old. She wants to take out an endowment policy over 20 years for £7500. How much will she pay as a monthly premium?

5 Tariq is 27 years old and Iqbal is 25. They both take out an endowment policy for £8000 over 25 years.
   (a) What is the monthly premium for each?
   (b) Who pays the greater premium?
   (c) Why do you think this is the case?

6 Terry will be 26 years old next month. He wants to take out a whole life policy for £4750.
   (a) How much is the monthly premium?
   (b) After how many months will he have paid £4750 to the assurance company?
   (c) How old will he be at this time?

Use the chess board below to solve these puzzles.

1 Rows, columns and diagonals

You need 8 counters.

Arrange the 8 counters so that no counters share the same row, column or diagonal.

Use the coordinate system to record your answer.

Ask another student to check your answer.

2 Squares of all sizes

How many squares can you find on a chess board?

■ Investigation

3 Find out about the Knight's Tour problem.

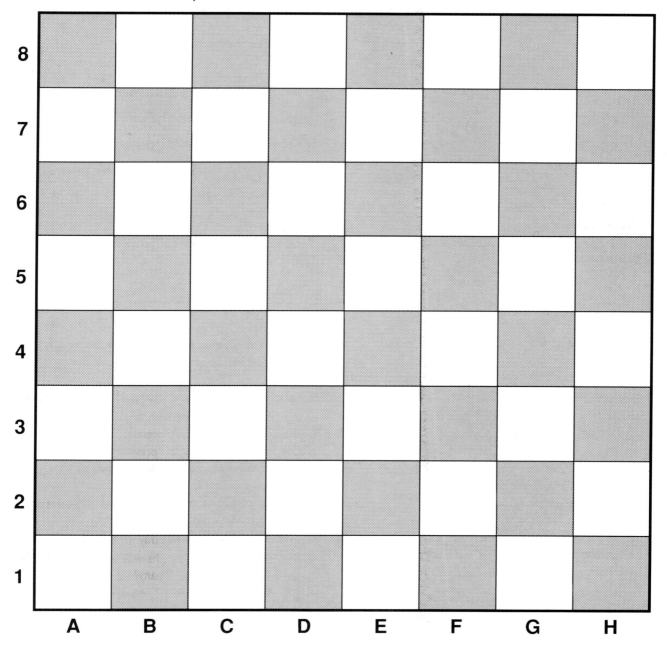

At the Church Fair Anne tries the Lucky Dip. The dip contains 36 lollipops, 20 key rings, 8 purses and 2 watches.

Probability of picking a purse

$$= \frac{\text{number of purses}}{\text{total number of items}}$$

$$= \frac{8}{66}$$

$$= \frac{4}{33}$$

P(purse) $= \frac{4}{33}$

1 At the Bottle stall every ticket wins a prize. Find the probability of winning a bottle of:

(a) wine   (b) ketchup

(c) perfume   (d) cooking oil.

2 Stanley's stall has 16 playing cards arranged on a board.

A blindfolded player throws a dart. If the dart pierces a card find:

(a) P(eight)   (b) P(ace)

(c) P(even number)   (d) P(King or Queen or Jack).

3 At the Hook-a-Duck stall Betty has 36 ducks numbered from 1 to 36.

For one try find:

(a) P(another try)   (b) P(50p)

(c) P(fluffy duck)   (d) P(nothing).

● Remember

Relative frequency is an estimate of probability.

---

4 Cathie has been watching the Hoopla stall. She watched 48 throws and 3 of them were winners.

(a) From Cathie's observations, what is the probability of winning at the Hoopla stall?

(b) Why is the probability of winning not the same for everyone?

5 Greta is selling Tombola tickets. She has 3000 to sell and 400 of them are winning numbers.
What is the probability of buying a winning ticket?

6 Find the probability of buying a winning Tombola ticket if there are:

(a) 5000 tickets with 500 winning numbers

(b) 4000 tickets with 800 winning numbers

(c) 2500 tickets with 300 winning numbers

(d) 1500 tickets with 150 winning numbers.

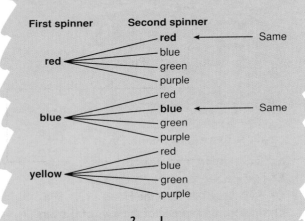

At the Spin and Win stall a player has to spin both spinners.
To find the probability of winning, a tree diagram can be drawn.

First spinner	Second spinner	
	red ←	Same
red	blue	
	green	
	purple	
	red	
blue	**blue** ←	Same
	green	
	purple	
	red	
yellow	blue	
	green	
	purple	

$$P(\text{same colour}) = \frac{2}{12} = \frac{1}{6}$$

7 For each pair of spinners:
• draw a tree diagram • find P(winning).

(a)

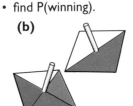

(b)

(c)

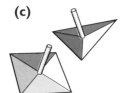

(d)

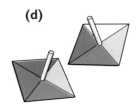

8 At the Pick-a-Marble stall Don picks a marble from each bag.
Bag A contains 3 marbles and bag B contains 4 marbles. Draw a tree diagram and find:
(a) P(two blues)   **(b)** P(two reds)
(c) P(one blue and one red).

9 At the Crack the Safe stall each player turns the dials. The winning combination is 242.

(a) Copy and complete the tree diagram to find all possible combinations.

First dial (Dial A)	Second dial (Dial B)	Third dial (Dial C)
		1
	1	2
	2	3
1	3	
	4	
2		

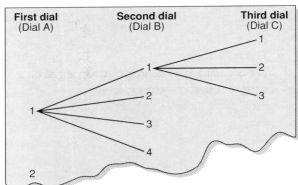

(b) What is the probability of opening the safe?

10 Nicola is rolling two dice.
(a) List all possible results.
(b) For each result calculate her total score.
(c) For the total scores find:
• P(7)   • P(10)   • P(12)   • P(5).

Probabilities of this *and* that

Mr Ford has set his class a series of problems on probability. For each problem students have to find the probability of **two independent events** occurring.

1 First Problem

Bill tosses a coin.
Kirsten throws a die.
The class investigates
P(tail and six).

(a) Find P(tail).
(b) Find P(six).
(c) Copy and complete this list of all possible outcomes.

head 1	head 2	head 3
tail 1	tail 2	t

(d) Find P(tail and six).

2 Second Problem

Jack tosses a coin.
Jill spins this spinner.
The class investigates
P(head and R).

(a) Find P(head).
(b) Find P(R).
(c) List all the possible outcomes when tossing a coin and spinning the spinner.
(d) Find P(head and R).

3 Third Problem

The bag contains 3 marbles, a red, a blue and a white.
Peter picks a marble without looking.
Lorna rolls a die.

The class investigates
P(white and one).

(a) Find P(white).
(b) Find P(one).
(c) List all the possible outcomes when picking a marble and rolling a die.
(d) Find P(white and one).

4 (a) Using your answers from the three problems, copy and complete the table.

	P(1st event)	P(2nd event)	P(1st and 2nd events)
Problem 1	$\frac{1}{2}$		
Problem 2			
Problem 3			

(b) What do you notice?

Mr Ford's class found:
P(1st event **and** 2nd event) = P(1st event) **x** P(2nd event)

5

The 4 aces from a pack of playing cards are placed face down and Adam has to choose one card.
Sarah spins the 5-sided spinner.

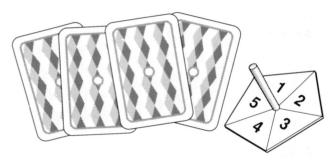

(a) Find: • P(Ace of Hearts) • P(5).
(b) Calculate P(Ace of Hearts and 5).

6

A coin is tossed and one of the days of the week is chosen at random.
(a) Find: • P(head) • P(Saturday).
(b) Calculate P(head and Saturday).

7

A die is rolled and one of the seven colours of the rainbow is chosen at random.
(a) Find: • P(six) • P(indigo).
(b) Calculate P(six and indigo).

8

A season of the year is chosen at random and a day of the week is also chosen at random.
(a) Find: • P(season beginning with W)
• P(day beginning with S).
(b) Calculate P(season beginning with W and day beginning with S).

Mr Ford has set his class a new set of problems about the probability of events which can occur in more than one way.

1 First Problem

Jimmy rolls a die.
The class investigates P(5 or 6). Find:

(a) P(5) **(b)** P(6) **(c)** P(5 or 6).

2 Second Problem

Sanjia chooses a counter at random from a bag containing 7 counters. The counters are white, red, yellow, green, brown, blue and black.

The class investigates P(white or black). Find:

(a) P(white) **(b)** P(black)
(c) P(white or black).

3 Third Problem

Sui picks a card from a pack of playing cards.

The class investigates P(seven or face). Find:

(a) P(seven) **(b)** P(face)
(c) P(seven or face).

4 Fourth Problem

Each letter of the word **MISSISSIPPI** is written on a card. Dymphna chooses a card at random.

The class investigates P(S or M). Find:

(a) P(S) **(b)** P(M) **(c)** P(S or M).

Mr Ford's class found:
P(1st event **or** 2nd event)
= P(1st event) **+** P(2nd event)

5 Check that your answers to the four problems fit this rule.

6 A bottle contains 25 red, 50 black, 12 blue and 13 green beads.
  (a) If a bead is picked at random find:
  • P(red) • P(black) • P(blue) • P(green).
  (b) Calculate:
  • P(red or black)
  • P(blue or green)
  • P(black or green)
  • P(black or blue or green)
  • P(red or black or blue or green).

7 A party of 50 people went on a theatre outing. They had a prize draw on the bus and each bought a ticket. There were 19 boys, 23 girls and 8 teachers.
Find the probability that the winner was:
  (a) a boy **(b)** a girl
  (c) a teacher **(d)** a student.

A problem shared

1 Brian has been given this diagram showing the floor of his new office.

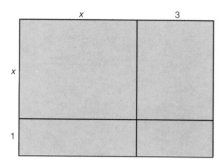

Find an expression for the floor area.

2 Paul's office is rectangular in shape. It measures $(x + 5)$ metres long and $(x - 1)$ metres broad. Find an expression, without brackets, for the floor area.

3 Sally bought $\frac{3}{5}$ kg of chocolate. She gave $\frac{1}{3}$ of this to her son and $\frac{1}{2}$ to her husband. Did she have enough chocolate left to give $\frac{1}{10}$ kg to her daughter?

4 Terry needs 5 litres of water to make soup. His measuring jug holds $\frac{3}{4}$ litre. How many full jugs of water will he measure out and how much more water will he still have to add?

5 Gemma is potting new plants. In each pot she mixes 3 parts of sand with 5 parts of peat.

(a) She has 900 g of sand and 1·7 kg of peat. How much peat will be left over if she uses all the sand?

(b) The mixture is to be divided equally into 16 pots. What weight of mixture will Gemma use in each pot?

6 Mumtaz designs containers. Here are two of his designs for a new milk carton.

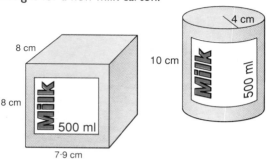

Round your answers to 3 significant figures.

(a) Calculate the volume of each carton. (Volume of a cylinder, $V = \pi r^2 h$)

(b) Calculate the surface area of each carton. (Area of a circle, $A = \pi r^2$)

(c) Which design would you choose? Give reasons for your answer.

7 Ralph has 5 pairs of socks in his drawer. They are coloured black, blue, grey, white and brown. He also has 2 pairs of black shoes and 1 brown pair. Draw a tree diagram and find the probability that when he chooses at random, Ralph will wear socks and shoes of the same colour.

8 Salwa is starting a new job. She is to be paid £4·46 per hour for a basic 36 hour week. Overtime is paid at time and a half. In her first week she works 43 hours. She expects to lose about $\frac{1}{3}$ of her gross pay in deductions. Estimate her net pay, to the nearest £.

9 Terri is designing a larger tin which is similar in shape to this one, but each dimension has been increased by a scale factor of 1·2. Will the new tin hold 1 litre of paint? Explain.

10 One hundred and twenty customers were interviewed at Homespun. Seventy-eight customers said they liked the range of goods on sale.

(a) Express this:
  • as a fraction in its simplest terms
  • as a decimal.

(b) What percentage of those interviewed did **not** like the range of goods on sale?

11 Wendy has bought a new car which she needs to insure. She has details from two different insurance companies.

Safeguard:	Basic premium £824
	Plus age payment 25% of basic premium
	No claims bonus 30% of the basic premium

Motorcare:	Basic premium £938
	No claims bonus 20% of basic premium
	Introductory discount 5% of net premium

Which company should she choose? Explain.

12 When Wendy ordered her car she was given a choice of these body colours: blue, red, white, green. She was also given a choice of these interior colours: grey, blue, black. In order to get a car quickly, Wendy agreed not to specify a colour scheme. If all the colours are equally likely, what is the probability that her car will be white, with either a grey or blue interior?

13

The advertisement gives the diameter of 2 sizes of circular pizza. Which size of pizza is the best value? Give a reason for your answer.

14

Find the angle between the hands of the clock when the time is:

(a) 5 o'clock   (b) half past ten.

15 Mark left home to drive to work. For the first 10 minutes he travelled at a steady speed along the by-pass. He then came to road works and was delayed for 5 minutes. He completed the rest of his journey at a steady, slower speed, arriving at work 35 minutes after leaving home. Copy and complete the graph.

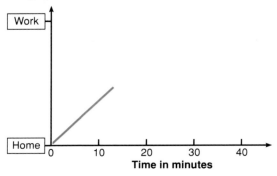

You need 2 mm graph paper.

For investigations and experiments, Zoe often draws graphs. The shape of the graph depends on the type of formula.

I Zoe investigated the formulae and graphs for two matchstick problems.

(a) Separate squares

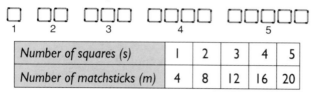

Number of squares (s)	1	2	3	4	5
Number of matchsticks (m)	4	8	12	16	20

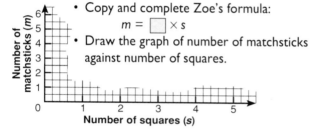

- Copy and complete Zoe's formula:
  $$m = \boxed{} \times s$$
- Draw the graph of number of matchsticks against number of squares.

(b) Linked squares

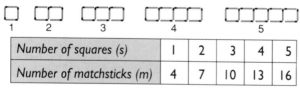

Number of squares (s)	1	2	3	4	5
Number of matchsticks (m)	4	7	10	13	16

- Copy and complete Zoe's formula:
  $$m = \boxed{} \times s + \boxed{}$$
- Draw the graph of number of matchsticks against number of squares.

2 Zoe investigated the number of 50 cm slabs needed to surround square flowerbeds.

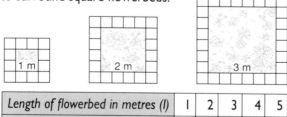

Length of flowerbed in metres (l)	1	2	3	4	5
Number of slabs (s)	12	20	28	36	44

(a) Copy and complete Zoe's formula:
$$s = \boxed{} \times l + \boxed{}$$
(b) Draw the graph of number of slabs against length of flowerbed.

Zoe's graphs are **straight lines**. They are the graphs of **linear functions**.

- **Formulae of the type y = ax**

  The graph is a straight line through the origin (0, 0).

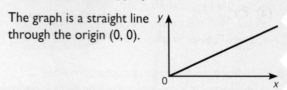

- **Formulae of the type y = ax + b**

  The graph is a straight line through (0, b).

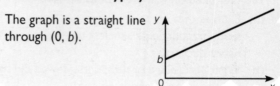

3 These are Zoe's results for an experiment about Ohm's Law.

Current (I)	0	1	2	3	4
Voltage (V)	0	2·5	5	7·5	10

(a) Copy and complete Zoe's formula for Ohm's Law:
$$V = \boxed{} \times I$$
(b) What type of graph would you expect?
(c) Draw the graph of voltage against current.

4 These are Zoe's results for an experiment about an accelerating object.

Time (t)	0	1	2	3	4
Velocity (v)	10	12	14	16	18

(a) Copy and complete Zoe's formula:
$$v = \boxed{} \times t + \boxed{}$$
(b) What type of graph would you expect?
(c) Draw the graph of velocity against time.

You need 2 mm graph paper.

1 Zoe investigated formulae and graphs in three tile problems.

(a) Pyramids

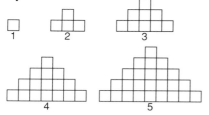

Pattern number (p)	1	2	3	4	5
Number of tiles (t)	1	4	9	16	25

- Check Zoe's formula: $t = p^2$
- Draw the graph of number of tiles against pattern number.

(b) Chimneys

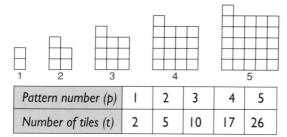

Pattern number (p)	1	2	3	4	5
Number of tiles (t)	2	5	10	17	26

- Copy and complete Zoe's formula:
  $$t = p^2 + \square$$
- Draw the graph of number of tiles against pattern number.

(c) Multilink

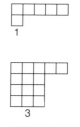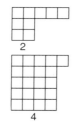

Pattern number (p)	1	2	3	4	5
Number of tiles (t)	6	9	14	21	30

- Copy and complete Zoe's formula:
  $$t = \square + \square$$
- Draw the graph of number of tiles against pattern number.

2 Zoe's teacher asked her to draw the graph of $y = x^2$ for values of x between $^-4$ and 4.

(a) Copy and complete Zoe's table.

x	$^-4$	$^-3$	$^-2$	$^-1$	0	1	2	3	4
y	16						4		

(b) Draw the graph of y against x.

Zoe's graphs are curves called **parabolas**. They are the graphs of **quadratic functions**.

- **Formulae of the type $y = x^2$**

  The graph is a parabola through the origin (0, 0).

  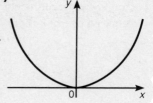

- **Formulae of the type $y = x^2 + b$**

  The graph is a parabola through the point (0, b).

  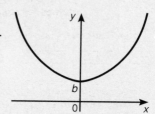

3 Zoe examined the shape of the inside surface of a curved mirror by calculating the height at different horizontal distances from the centre.

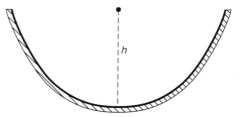

Distance from the centre (d)	$^-4$	$^-3$	$^-2$	$^-1$	0	1	2	3	4
Height (h)	20	13	8	5	4	5	8	13	20

(a) Copy and complete Zoe's formula:
  $$h = \square + \square$$

(b) What type of graph would you expect?

(c) Draw the graph of height against distance from the centre.

Zoe's cubes

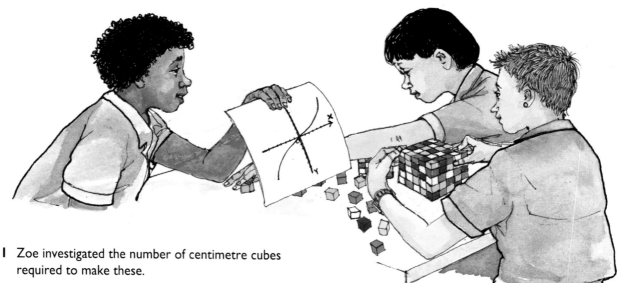

1 Zoe investigated the number of centimetre cubes required to make these.

1 cm

2 cm

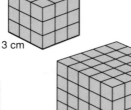

3 cm

4 cm

5 cm

Edge length (l)	1	2	3	4	5
Number of cm cubes (n)	1	8	27	64	125

(a) Check Zoe's formula: $n = l^3$

(b) Draw the graph of number of cm cubes against edge length.

2 Zoe's teacher asked her to draw the graph of $y = x^3$ for values of x between $^-4$ and 4.

(a) Copy and complete Zoe's table.

x	$^-4$	$^-3$	$^-2$	$^-1$	0	1	2	3	4
y	$^-64$			$^-1$				27	

(b) Draw the graph of y against x.

3 Zoe decided to draw the graph of $y = x^3 + 4$.

(a) Copy and complete Zoe's table.

x	$^-4$	$^-3$	$^-2$	$^-1$	0	1	2	3	4
y	$^-60$		3					31	

(b) Draw the graph of y against x.

These are graphs of **cubic functions**.

- **Formulae of the type $y = x^3$**

  The graph is a curve with this shape passing through the origin (0, 0).

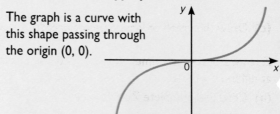

- **Formulae of the type $y = x^3 + b$**

  The graph is a curve with this shape, passing through (0, b).

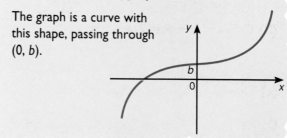

4 (a) Copy and complete this table for the formula $y = x^3 + 10$

x	$^-4$	$^-3$	$^-2$	$^-1$	0	1	2	3	4
y	$^-54$						18		

(b) Draw the graph of y against x.

5 (a) Make a table of values for the formula $y = x^3 - 10$

(b) Draw the graph of y against x.

1 Zoe investigated the lengths and breadths of rectangles, all of which have an area of 24 cm².

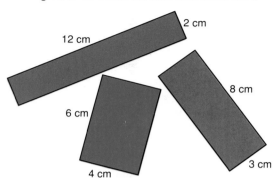

2 cm

12 cm

8 cm

6 cm

3 cm

4 cm

(a) Copy and complete Zoe's table.

Breadth in cm (b)	1	2	3	4	5	6
Length in cm (l)		12				

(b) Check Zoe's formula:

$$l = \frac{24}{b}$$

(c) Draw the graph of length against breadth.

2 Zoe investigated the time taken for a 60 km journey at different speeds.

(a) Copy and complete Zoe's table.

Speed in km/h (s)	10	20	30	40	50	60
Time in hours (t)				1·5		

(b) Copy and complete Zoe's formula:

$$t = \frac{60}{\boxed{}}$$

(c) Draw the graph of time against speed.

3 During the winter season Zoe can afford to spend a total of £48 on visits to the opera.

(a) Copy and complete Zoe's table.

Seat price in £ (p)	3	4	6	8	12	16
Number of visits (v)						

(b) Copy and complete Zoe's formula:

$$v = \frac{\boxed{}}{\boxed{}}$$

(c) Draw the graph of number of visits against seat price.

Zoe's graphs are curves called **hyperbolas**. They are the graphs of **reciprocal functions**.

- **Formulae of the type $y = \dfrac{a}{x}$**

The graph is a **hyperbola**.

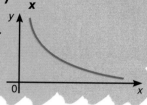

4 Zoe's teacher asked her to draw the graph of

$$y = \frac{1}{x}$$

(a) Copy and complete Zoe's table.

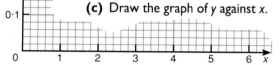

x	1	2	3	4	5	6	7	8	10
y				0·25					0·1

(b) What type of graph would you expect?

(c) Draw the graph of y against x.

5 These are Zoe's results for an electricity experiment.

Resistance (R)	2	3	4	5	6
Current (I)	9	6	4·5	3·6	3

(a) Copy and complete Zoe's formula:

$$I = \frac{\boxed{}}{\boxed{}}$$

(b) What type of graph would you expect to find?

(c) Draw the graph of current against resistance.

6 These are Zoe's results for an experiment about Boyle's Law.

Volume (V)	15	18	22·5	30	45
Pressure (P)	3	2·5	2	1·5	1

(a) Copy and complete Zoe's formula:

$$P = \frac{\boxed{}}{\boxed{}}$$

(b) What type of graph would you expect to find?

(c) Draw the graph of pressure against volume.

Pair each formula with its graph.

1. $y = x^3 - 1$

2. $y = x^2$

3. $a = 8t - 12$

4. $T = \dfrac{80}{S}$

5. $V = l^3$

6. $P = 4l$

7. $h = d^2 + 20$

8. $p = q^3 + 5$

9. $C = 5n + 6$

10. $d = l^2 - 10$

This is part of the graph of $y = 5x + 2$

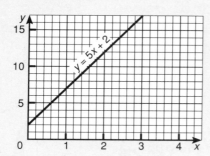

For every point on the graph,
y coordinate = 5 times x coordinate + 2
(**4, 22**) lies on the graph since **22** = 5 × **4** + 2

When $x = 3$, $y = 5 \times 3 + 2$
          $= 15 + 2$
          $= 17$
The point (**3, 17**) lies on the graph of $y = 5x + 2$

1 (**a**) Which points lie on the graph $y = 5x + 2$?
   • (2, 12)   • (6, 40)   • (8, 42)   • (12, 62)
(**b**) Find the coordinates of each point on the graph
   when the x coordinate is:
   • 0   • 1   • 7   • 10

2 This is part of the graph of $y = x^2 + 3$

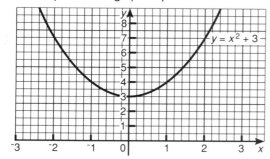

(**a**) Which points lie on the graph $y = x^2 + 3$?
   • (2, 7)   • (⁻1, 4)   • (10, 169)   • (⁻5, ⁻22)
(**b**) Find the coordinates of each point on the graph
   when the x coordinate is:
   • 0   • 1   • ⁻3   • 4

3 (**a**) Which points lie on the graph $y = x^2 - 2$?
   • (⁻1, ⁻4)   • (3, 7)   • (4, 16)   • (⁻10, 98)
(**b**) Find the coordinates of each point on the graph
   when the x coordinate is:
   • 0   • 1   • 2   • ⁻3

4 This is part of the graph of $y = x^3 - 1$

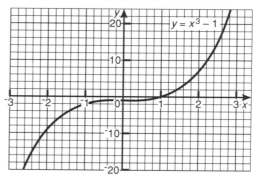

(**a**) Which points lie on the graph $y = x^3 - 1$?
   • (2, 5)   • (3, 26)   • (4, 63)   • (⁻3, ⁻28)
(**b**) Find the coordinates of each point on the graph
   when the x coordinate is:
   • 0   • 1   • ⁻2   • 5

5 (**a**) Which points lie on the graph $y = x^3 + 5$?
   • (1, 6)   • (⁻2, ⁻3)   • (3, 14)   • (⁻10, ⁻1005)
(**b**) Find the coordinates of each point on the graph
   when the x coordinate is:
   • 0   • 2   • ⁻3   • 5

6 This is part of the graph of $y = \dfrac{30}{x}$

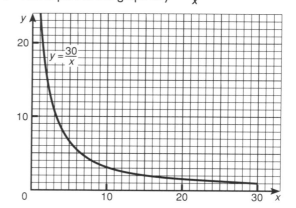

(**a**) Which points lie on the graph $y = \dfrac{30}{x}$?
   • (2, 15)   • (5, 6)   • (15, 3)   • (0·5, 60)
(**b**) Find the coordinates of each point on the graph
   when the x coordinate is:
   • 1   • 6   • 10   • 12

Red Dragon Transport

Cyndwen (Red Dragon)

> I work for Red Dragon Transport, planning the 24-hour parcel service. Vans follow a circular route connecting our 8 depots. We have a timetable to give a full pick-up and delivery service.

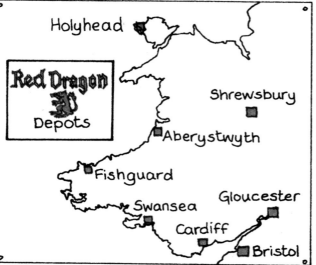

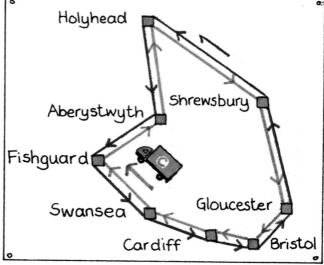

Clockwise Red Dragon Transport / Anticlockwise

Clockwise	C_1	C_2	C_3
CARDIFF		0400	1230
Swansea		0450 / 0505	1330 / 1345
Fishguard		0710 / 0725	1555 / 1610
Aberystwyth		0915 / 0930	1810 / 1825
Holyhead	0500	1230 / 1245	2115 / 2130
Shrewsbury	0745 / 0800	1540 / 1555	0015 / 0030
Gloucester	1000 / 1015	1755 / 1810	0215 / 0230
Bristol	1105 / 1120	1900 / 1915	0310 / 0325
CARDIFF	1215	2010	0420

Anticlockwise	A_1	A_2	A_3
CARDIFF		0030	0930
Bristol		0125 / 0140	1035 / 1050
Gloucester		0220 / 0235	1145 / 1200
Shrewsbury		0425 / 0440	1405 / 1420
Holyhead	0100	0735 / 0750	1720 / 1735
Aberystwyth	0350 / 0405	1100 / 1115	2040 / 2055
Fishguard	0545 / 0600	1250 / 1305	2245 / 2300
Swansea	0755 / 0810	1500 / 1515	0050 / 0105
CARDIFF	0915	1625	0145

1 (a) How long is allowed for loading and unloading at each depot?

(b) Is it quicker to go from Holyhead to Cardiff via Gloucester or via Fishguard?

(c) How many vans go each day from Holyhead to Cardiff?

(d) How many vans each day go **directly** from:
- Aberystwyth to Fishguard
- Fishguard to Aberystwyth?

(e) Which vans leave Cardiff one day and arrive back the next day?

2 How long does van C_2 take to travel from:

(a) Cardiff to Aberystwyth

(b) Gloucester to Cardiff

(c) Swansea to Holyhead?

3 What is the shortest journey time between:

(a) Cardiff and Swansea

(b) Gloucester and Holyhead

(c) Cardiff and Fishguard

(d) Fishguard and Holyhead?

Van A_3 leaves Cardiff at 0930 and arrives in Shrewsbury at 1405. Cyndwen calculates the journey time using a time line.

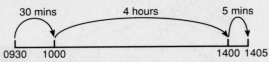

Total time = 30 minutes + 4 hours + 5 minutes.
The journey time is **4 hours 35 minutes**.

4 Calculate the times for these van journeys.
  (a) Leaves Holyhead 0750, arrives Swansea 1500
  (b) Leaves Shrewsbury 1555, arrives Cardiff 2010
  (c) Leaves Swansea 1345, arrives Holyhead 2115
  (d) Leaves Holyhead 1245, arrives Cardiff 2010
  (e) Leaves Bristol 1050, arrives Aberystwyth 2040

5 Calculate the times for these journeys.
  (a) Van C_2 from Fishguard to Bristol
  (b) Van C_3 from Cardiff to Holyhead
  (c) Van A_2 from Bristol to Holyhead
  (d) Van A_3 from Bristol to Fishguard

Van C_3 leaves Fishguard at 1610 and arrives in Cardiff at 0420.

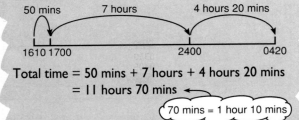

Total time = 50 mins + 7 hours + 4 hours 20 mins
           = 11 hours 70 mins
           (70 mins = 1 hour 10 mins)

The journey time is **12 hours 10 minutes**.

6 Calculate the journey time for:
  (a) van A_3 from Fishguard to Cardiff
  (b) van A_3 from Gloucester to Swansea
  (c) van C_3 from Holyhead to Gloucester
  (d) van C_3 from Aberystwyth to Shrewsbury.

7 A parcel in the Bristol depot must be delivered in Holyhead before 8 am. Which van should be used and when does it leave Bristol?

8 Which van has the shortest journey time for the round trip from Cardiff? How long does it take?

Red Dragon's long-haul division operates from their Cardiff depot. Trucks run regularly to the towns on the map.

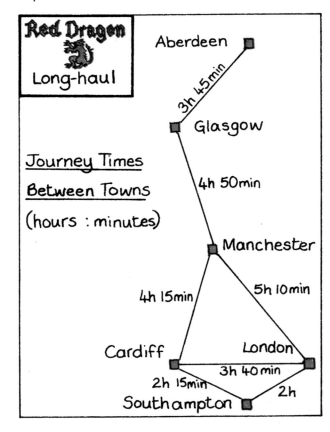

  (a) Cardiff to London
  (b) Glasgow to London
  (c) Aberdeen to Manchester
  (d) Glasgow to Southampton via Cardiff
  (e) Cardiff to Aberdeen?

10 Find the arrival time of a truck which leaves:
  (a) Glasgow for Aberdeen at 1 pm
  (b) Cardiff for London at 0830
  (c) Cardiff for Manchester at 2030
  (d) London for Manchester at 9.30 pm
  (e) Cardiff for Glasgow at 0540
  (f) Manchester for Aberdeen at 10 pm
  (g) Aberdeen for Cardiff at 1045.

11 Gareth leaves Cardiff for Glasgow at 1430. He spends $8\frac{1}{2}$ hours in Glasgow, then returns to Cardiff. When does he arrive back in Cardiff?

Timing it right

● **Remember**

There are **60 minutes in 1 hour**.

> not 2h 25mins

- 2·25 hours = $2\frac{1}{4}$ hours
  = 2 hours 15 minutes

- 0·8 hours = 0·8 × 60 mins
  = 48 mins

  3·8 hours = 3 hours 48 minutes

1 Change these times to hours and minutes.

(a) 2·5 hours   (b) 3·75 hours   (c) 0·7 hours

(d) 1·2 hours   (e) 4·9 hours   (f) 2·3 hours

- 24 mins = $\frac{24}{60}$ hours = 0·4 hours
  4 hours 24 minutes = 4·4 hours

- 25 mins = $\frac{25}{60}$ hours = 0·416667

  = 0·42 hours rounded to 2 decimal places.

2 Change these times to hours. Round to 2 dp where necessary.

(a) 2 hours 36 minutes   (b) 1 hour 6 minutes

(c) 3 hours 50 minutes   (d) 5 hours 3 minutes

(e) 2 hours 20 minutes   (f) 4 hours 28 minutes

During a journey vehicles speed up, slow down and at times stop.

$$\text{Average speed} = \frac{\text{Distance}}{\text{Total time taken}}$$

3 Calculate the average speeds of Red Dragon trucks on these journeys.

(a) Cardiff – Birmingham   100 miles in 2 hours

(b) Cardiff – Stoke   144 miles in 3 hours

(c) Cardiff – Stranraer   400 miles in 10 hours

(d) Cardiff – Fort William   504 miles in 12 hours

(e) Cardiff – Carlisle   299 miles in $6\frac{1}{2}$ hours

(f) Cardiff – Gloucester   60 miles in $1\frac{1}{2}$ hours

(g) Cardiff – Oxford   108 miles in 2 hours 15 min

(h) Cardiff – Manchester   190 miles in 4 hours 45 min

4 Use the information in Ieuan's log to calculate the average speed for each trip he makes.

DRIVER'S LOG

Red Dragon
Long-haul

Name _Ieuan Jones_

6/11/94	Cardiff / 0600	Glasgow / 1500	396
7/11/94	Glasgow / 0830	Leeds / 1400	220
7/11/94	Leeds / 1815	Cardiff / 2315	225
9/11/94	Cardiff / 1010	Swansea / 1058	40
9/11/94	Swansea / 1300	Milford Haven / 1430	60
9/11/94	Milford Haven / 1500	Cardiff / 1806	93
10/11/94	Cardiff / 0715	Dover / 1600	245
11/11/94	Dover / 0930	Cardiff / 1642	252

5 Owen drives for Red Dragon's international division. Calculate the average speed, to the nearest km per hour, for each leg of his journey.

DRIVER'S LOG

Red Dragon
International

Name _Owen A. Hughes_

Date	From / Departure time	To / Arrival time	Distance (km)
20/10/94	Cardiff / 0345	Portsmouth / 0730	210
20/10/94	Portsmouth / 0830 (SHIP)	Caen / 1415	160
20/10/94	Caen / 1500	Paris / 1820	240
21/10/94	Paris / 1100	Roscoff / 2215	565
21/10/94	Roscoff / 2330 (SHIP)	Plymouth / 0530	180
22/10/94	Plymouth / 0610	Cardiff / 0958	266

● **Remember**   Time = $\dfrac{\text{Distance}}{\text{Speed}}$

1 Red Dragon runs an overnight express parcel service from Cardiff.
For each journey calculate the time in hours and minutes, given the distance and average speed.
(a) London, 153 miles at 51 mph
(b) Liverpool, 196 miles at 49 mph
(c) Edinburgh, 391 miles at 46 mph
(d) Birmingham, 105 miles at 60 mph

2 I estimate our trucks can average these speeds:
 • 50 mph on motorway journeys under 100 miles
 • 46 mph on motorway journeys over 100 miles
 • 40 mph on main roads
 • 35 mph on minor roads

For each journey calculate the time in hours and minutes.
(a) Edinburgh to Sunderland
    120 miles on the main A1 road
(b) Carlisle to Shrewsbury
    184 miles on the M6 and M54
(c) London to Birmingham
    115 miles on the M40
(d) Bristol to Exeter
    75 miles on the M5
(e) Oxford to Southampton
    70 miles on the main A34 road
(f) Cardiff to Swansea
    40 miles on the M5
(g) Llandovery to Oswestry
    77 miles on minor roads
(h) Exeter to Barnstaple
    42 miles on minor roads

3 Mark leaves Cardiff with a load of engine parts for Dagenham. When is the latest he can leave?

Ref _ _ _ _
Depart
Cardiff _ _ _ _ _ _
Distance _207 miles_
Av. speed _46 mph_
Arrive
Dagenham _4 pm_ _ _ _

4 Compuware are sending a software package from Cardiff to the Harwich ferry which sails for Germany at 0700. Cardiff is 246 miles from Harwich and the van should average 50 mph. Cyndwen tells the driver to leave at 3 am. Will he be on time? Explain.

● **Remember**   **Distance = Speed × Time**

5 Calculate the distance travelled by each Red Dragon truck:
(b) Cardiff to Norwich,
    average speed of 39 mph for 7 hours
(b) Cardiff to Penzance,
    average speed of 44 mph for $5\frac{1}{2}$ hours
(c) Cardiff to Sheffield,
    average speed of 48 mph for 4 hours and 15 minutes.

6 On his return journey to Cardiff from Edinburgh David picked up goods in these towns. Calculate the distance he travelled on each leg of the journey.

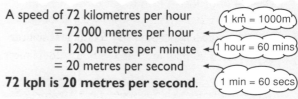

A speed of 72 kilometres per hour
= 72 000 metres per hour ← 1 km = 1000m
= 1200 metres per minute ← 1 hour = 60 mins
= 20 metres per second ←
72 kph is 20 metres per second.   1 min = 60 secs

7 Change each speed to metres per second.
(a) 36 kph   (b) 54 kph   (c) 90 kph

▶ **Challenge**

8 (a) The driver of a lorry travelling at 80 kph sees a crash ahead and takes **1 second** to put his foot on the brake.
    How far does the lorry travel in this time?
(b) The driver of a van travelling at 100 kph glances at a road map for **2 seconds**.
    How far does the van travel in this time?
(c) The driver of a car travelling at 120 kph takes **3 seconds** to read a road sign.
    How far does the car travel in 3 seconds?

For each route I have a graph which shows travel times. This is the graph for Monmouth to Cardiff.

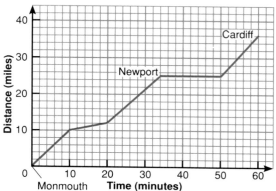

1 **(a)** What is the distance between:
- Monmouth and Newport
- Newport and Cardiff?

(b) How long is the stop in Newport?

2 There are major roadworks between Monmouth and Newport.

(a) What distance do they cover?

(b) How long does it take to get through them?

3 This is the graph for the journey from Pembroke to Brecon.

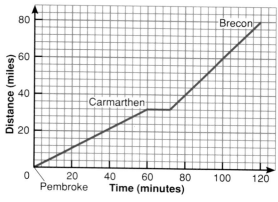

(a) What is the distance between Pembroke and Brecon?

(b) Which part of the journey is the slowest?

(c) What distance is covered in the first half hour?

(d) If there were no stop in Carmarthen, how long would the journey take?

The graph shows the journey from Swansea to Monmouth.

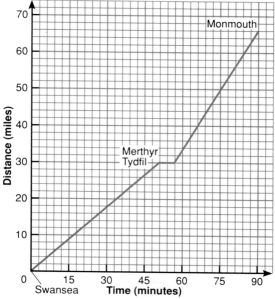

Find:

(a) the total journey time

(b) the total distance travelled

(c) the length of time spent in Merthyr Tydfil

(d) the slower section of the journey.

5 The graph shows the return journey from Dolgellau to Colwyn Bay via Wrexham.

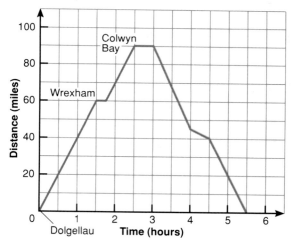

(a) Find the distance between:
- Dolgellau and Wrexham
- Wrexham and Colwyn Bay.

(b) How long does it take to travel from Wrexham to Colwyn Bay?

(c) What distance is covered in the last half hour?

The graph shows the journey from Aberystwyth to Caernarvon.

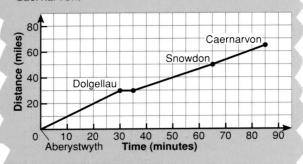

From Dolgellau to Snowdon
• the distance is 20 miles
• the time taken is 30 minutes.

$$\text{Speed} = \frac{\text{distance}}{\text{time}}$$

$$= \frac{20 \text{ miles}}{0.5 \text{ hours}} \longleftarrow \text{30 minutes is 0·5 hours}$$

$$= 40 \text{ miles per hour}$$

Average speed is **40 mph**.

1 Between Aberystwyth and Dolgellau find:
   (a) the distance
   (b) the time taken
   (c) the average speed.

2 Repeat question 1 for the journey between Snowdon and Caernarvon.

3 From Aberystwyth to Caernarvon find:
   (a) the total distance
   (b) the time for the journey **excluding** stops
   (c) the average speed.

4 The graph shows the route from Carmarthen to Swansea.

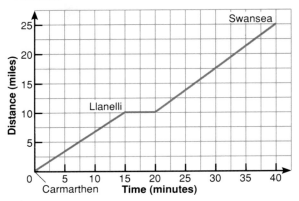

(a) Copy and complete the table.

From	To	Distance (miles)	Time (min)	Speed (mph)
Carmarthen	Llanelli	10		
Llanelli	Swansea			
Carmarthen	Swansea (non-stop)			

(b) If a van leaves Llanelli at 2.30 pm when should it arrive in Swansea?

5 From this graph find the average speed travelled between:
   (a) Brecon and Monmouth (b) Monmouth and Newport.

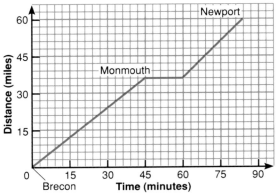

Count the miles

Cyndwen uses a mileage chart to find the shortest distance between two towns.

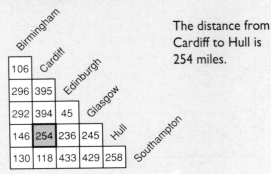

The distance from Cardiff to Hull is 254 miles.

1 Use the chart to find the distance between:
 (a) Birmingham and Hull
 (b) Edinburgh and Southampton
 (c) Glasgow and Hull
 (d) Cardiff and Glasgow.

▶ **You need Worksheet 5.**

2 The mileage chart gives the distances between the towns shown on the map in question **1** on Worksheet 5.

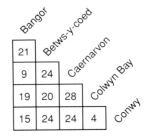

Find the value of each missing distance and write it on the map.

3 Use the map to find the values missing from the chart in question **2** on Worksheet 5.

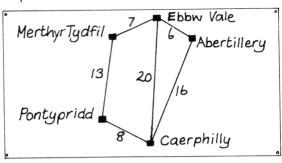

4 For each map complete the mileage charts in question **3** on Worksheet 5.
 (a)

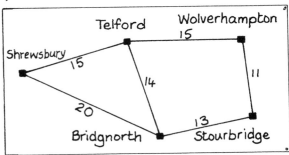

 (b)

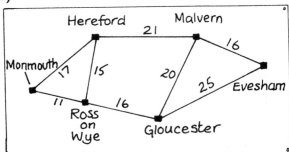

5 For this map complete the mileage chart in question **4** on Worksheet 5.

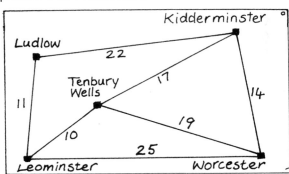

▼ **Challenge**

6 For this mileage chart create a suitable map.

	Bridgend	Maesteg	Neath	Port Talbot	Porthcawl
	9				
	17	8			
	14	15	7		
	7	15	16	9	

Cyndwen uses this table to find transport costs.

Red Dragon Transport	Transport costs (£) Distance (miles)				
	10	20	30	40	50
Weight of load (kg) 50	18	22	26	30	34
100	24	30	36	42	48
200	32	40	48	56	64
500	60	75	90	100	110
1000	100	120	140	180	220

To transport 100 kg a distance of 40 miles the cost is £42.

1 Use Cyndwen's table to find the cost of transporting:
   (a) 200 kg for 20 miles
   (b) 500 kg for 50 miles
   (c) 1200 kg for 80 miles.

2 The hourly rate of pay for drivers is based on the number of years of service and the type of driving: local, short-haul, long-haul or international.

Red Dragon Transport	Hourly rate (£) Years of service					
	0	1	2	3	4	5 or more
Local	5	5·25	5·50	5·90	6	6·50
Short-haul	5·20	5·50	5·80	6	6·30	6·90
Long-haul	6	6·50	6·90	7	7·80	8·30
International	6·50	7	7·80	8·30	8·80	9·30

   (a) For each driver find the hourly rate.
       Claire: 3 years service, local
       Sam: 1 years service, long-haul
       James: 8 years service, international
   (b) Fred drives short-haul and has 2 years' service. How much does he earn for a 35 hour week?

Red Dragon Transport hires out self-drive vans.

3 Use the chart to find the charges, excluding VAT, for:
   (a) an Economy van for two days
   (b) a Standard van for five days
   (c) a Mega van for eight days.

4 Georgina paid for a Standard van for three days and then paid for another four days. How much would she have saved, excluding VAT, if she had hired it for seven days without a break?

5 Linda has calculated that she needs a Standard van for four days or an Economy van for five.
   Which is cheaper?

6 Gary paid £82·25 to hire a van. This price includes VAT at 17·5%.
   Which van did he hire and for how long?

▶ Challenge

7 In one week Cyndwen made £174 (excluding VAT) on one-day van hires.
   Which vans were hired out, for how many times?

Hexaflexagon

▶ **You need Worksheet 6.**

Step 1
Cut around the perimeter of shape 1.

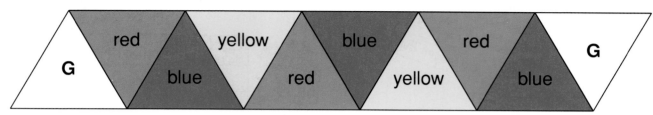

Step 2
Make a crease, forward and backward, along each line.

Step 3
Colour each triangle, front and back as shown.
Colour the back of the tabs G in yellow.

Step 4
Fold the yellow triangle under the blue triangle to make this shape.

Step 5
Fold the blue triangle over the yellow triangle tucking the tab G behind the top blue triangle.

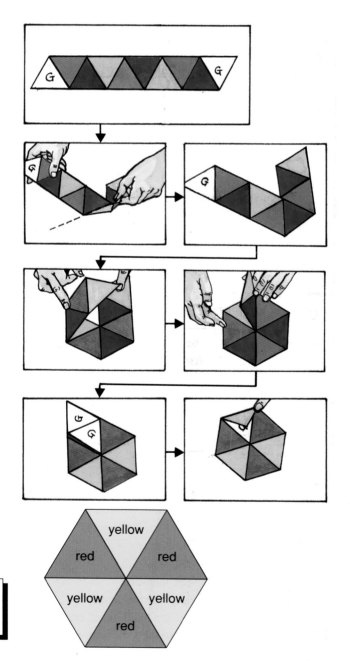

Step 6
Turn over your shape. Fold and glue the tabs G together.

• Your hexaflexagon is now ready for use.
• Flex your hexaflexagon to show other combinations of colours.

Repeat the steps with the other shapes on **Worksheet 6** to make other hexaflexagons.

The hexaflexagon was invented by Professor Arthur H Stone in 1939, while he was a student.

In the adventure playground the ramp has three supports.
The sketch shows the side view of the ramp.

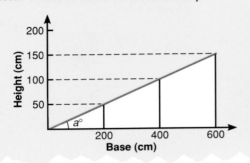

● Remember

Triangles which are similar contain the same angles.
The sketch shows how the ramp forms three
similar triangles.

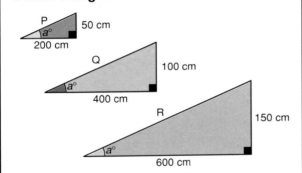

I Copy and complete the table.

Triangle	height (cm)	base (cm)	Ratio = $\dfrac{height}{base}$
P	50	200	$\dfrac{50}{200} = 0.25$
Q	100		
R			

The ratio $\dfrac{height}{base}$ is the same for each

of the similar right-angled triangles.

The ratio $\dfrac{\textbf{height}}{\textbf{base}}$ is called the **tangent** of angle a.

It is written **tan $a° = 0.25$**.

2 ▶ Do Worksheet 7, question I.

In right-angled triangles the tangent ratio can be
found by dividing the height by the base.

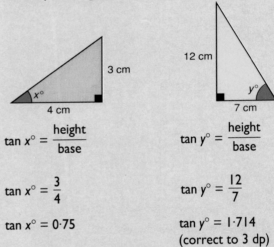

$$\tan x° = \frac{height}{base}$$

$$\tan x° = \frac{3}{4}$$

$$\tan x° = 0.75$$

$$\tan y° = \frac{height}{base}$$

$$\tan y° = \frac{12}{7}$$

$$\tan y° = 1.714$$
(correct to 3 dp)

3 Find the tangent of the marked angle in each triangle.
Round answers correct to 3 dp where necessary.

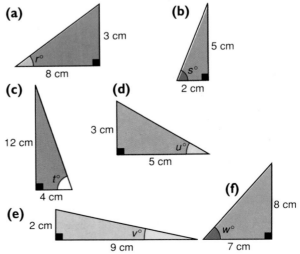

Often it is not appropriate to use 'height' and 'base' to describe sides in a right-angled triangle.

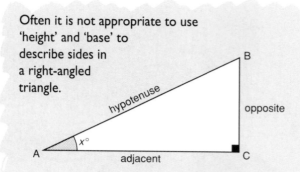

- the longest side AB is called the **hypotenuse**
- the side BC opposite angle $x°$ is called the **opposite** side
- the remaining side AC is called the **adjacent** side

1 In each triangle name the hypotenuse.

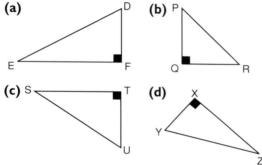

(a) **(b)** **(c)** **(d)**

2 In each triangle name the side opposite angle x.

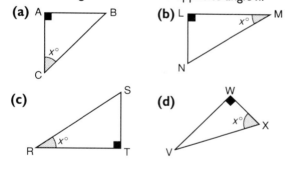

(a) **(b)** **(c)** **(d)**

3 In each triangle name the side adjacent to angle p.

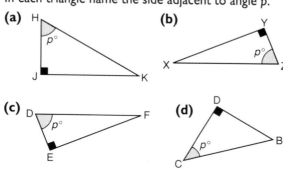

(a) **(b)** **(c)** **(d)**

In a right-angled triangle

$$\tan x° = \frac{\text{opposite side}}{\text{adjacent side}}$$

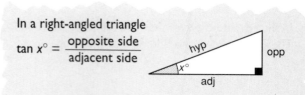

To find $\tan y°$ label the hypotenuse, opposite and adjacent sides.

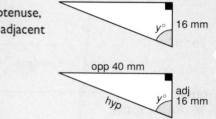

$$\tan y° = \frac{\text{opp}}{\text{adj}}$$

$$\tan y° = \frac{40}{16}$$

$$\tan y° = 2\cdot5$$

4 For each triangle:
- sketch the diagram
- label the hypotenuse, opposite and adjacent sides
- find $\tan w°$.

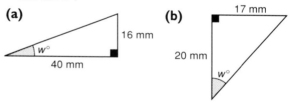

(a) **(b)**

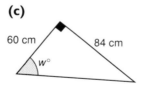 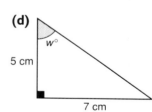

(c) **(d)**

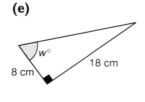 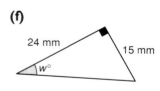

(e) **(f)**

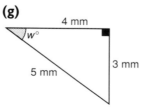 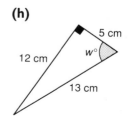

(g) **(h)**

If the size of the angle is known, the tangent ratio can be found using a calculator.

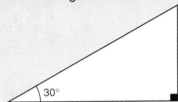

To find tan 30°

Enter **30** Press **tan** to give **0.5773502**

tan 30° is 0·577 correct to 3 decimal places.

1 Find, correct to 3 decimal places:
   (a) tan 20°   (b) tan 53°   (c) tan 84°
   (d) tan 72°   (e) tan 34·5°   (f) tan 69·2°
   (g) tan 45°   (h) tan 85·7°   (i) tan 0°.

We can use the tangent ratio to find the size of an angle.

$$\tan a° = \frac{opp}{adj}$$

$$\tan a° = \frac{11}{14}$$

$$\tan a° = \boxed{0.7857142}$$

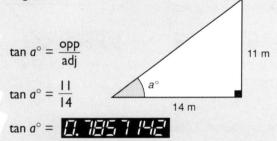

Do not clear the display.

To find the size of angle $a°$

Press **INV** Press $\overset{\tan^{-1}}{\boxed{\text{tan}}}$ to give **38.157227**

Angle $a = 38·2°$ correct to 1 decimal place.

2 Find the size of each angle correct to one decimal place.

tan $a°$ = 0·575	tan $b°$ = 1·320
tan $c°$ = 0·900	tan $d°$ = 1·000
tan $e°$ = 0·813	tan $f°$ = 4·134
tan $g°$ = 31·821	tan $h°$ = 0·275
tan $i°$ = 3·895	tan $j°$ = 1·732

3 Find the size of each marked angle correct to one decimal place.

(a)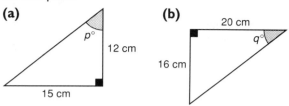

(b)

(c)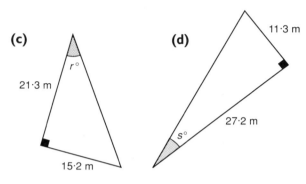

(d)

4 William has designed a fort for the adventure playground. The foot of the ladder is 1·7 m from the wall and reaches 2·6 m up the wall.
Calculate the angle the ladder makes with the ground.

5 Beside the fort is a flagpole 5 m high. The guy-ropes are anchored 1·75 m from the foot of the pole. Calculate the angle between a guy-rope and the ground.

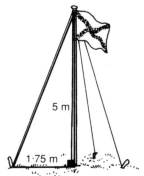

Another angle on trig

William has a ladder 3·2 m long which reaches 2·6 m up the wall of the fort. What is the angle between the ladder and the ground?

This time the **opposite** side and the **hypotenuse** are known.

The ratio $\dfrac{\text{opposite}}{\text{hypotenuse}}$ is called the **sine** of angle $a°$.

This is written $\quad \sin a° = \dfrac{\text{opposite}}{\text{hypotenuse}}$

$$\sin a° = \frac{2·6}{3·2}$$

$$\sin a° = \boxed{0.8125}$$

Do not clear the display.

To find the size of angle $a°$

Press **INV** Press **sin** $\overset{\sin^{-1}}{}$ to give $\boxed{54.340912}$

The angle between the ladder and the ground is **54·4°** correct to 1 decimal place.

This ramp is 2·8 m long. It starts 1·9 m from the foot of the support. William has to calculate the angle the ramp makes with the ground.

This time the **adjacent** side and the **hypotenuse** are known.

The ratio $\dfrac{\text{adjacent}}{\text{hypotenuse}}$ is called the **cosine** of angle $a°$.

This is written $\quad \cos a° = \dfrac{\text{adjacent}}{\text{hypotenuse}}$

$$\cos a° = \frac{1·9}{2·8}$$

$$\cos a° = \boxed{0.6785714}$$

Do not clear the display.

To find the size of angle $a°$

Press **INV** Press **cos** $\overset{\cos^{-1}}{}$ to give $\boxed{47.26789}$

The angle the ramp makes with the ground is **47·3°** correct to 1 decimal place.

1 Find, correct to 3 decimal places:
   (a) $\sin 27°$ (b) $\sin 39°$ (c) $\sin 60°$
   (d) $\sin 78·6°$ (e) $\sin 84·2°$ (f) $\sin 32·9°$

2 Find the size of each angle correct to 1 dp.
   $\sin a° = 0·500$ $\sin b° = 0·785$
   $\sin c° = 0·867$ $\sin d° = 0·922$
   $\sin e° = 0·562$ $\sin f° = 0·309$
   $\sin g° = 0·707$ $\sin h° = 0·494$
   $\sin i° = 0·818$ $\sin j° = 0·099$

3 Find the size of each marked angle correct to 1 dp.

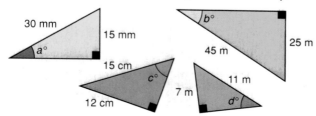

4 Find, correct to 3 decimal places:
   (a) $\cos 32°$ (b) $\cos 57°$ (c) $\cos 54·2°$
   (d) $\cos 45°$ (e) $\cos 73·9°$ (f) $\cos 87·4°$

5 Find the size of each angle correct to 1 dp.
   $\cos a° = 0·790$ $\cos b° = 0·543$
   $\cos c° = 0·838$ $\cos d° = 0·771$
   $\cos e° = 0·367$ $\cos f° = 0·036$
   $\cos g° = 1$ $\cos h° = 0·977$
   $\cos i° = 0·5$ $\cos j° = 0$

6 Find the size of each marked angle correct to 1 dp.

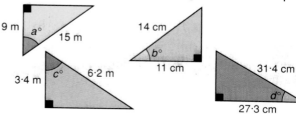

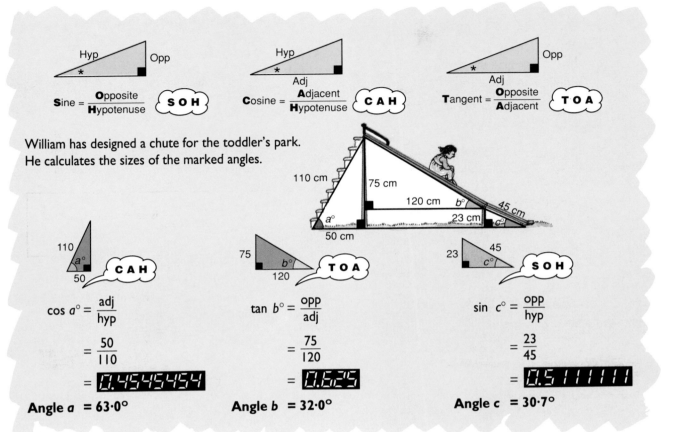

Sine = $\dfrac{\textbf{Opposite}}{\textbf{Hypotenuse}}$ **SOH**

Cosine = $\dfrac{\textbf{Adjacent}}{\textbf{Hypotenuse}}$ **CAH**

Tangent = $\dfrac{\textbf{Opposite}}{\textbf{Adjacent}}$ **TOA**

William has designed a chute for the toddler's park.
He calculates the sizes of the marked angles.

CAH

$\cos a° = \dfrac{adj}{hyp}$

$= \dfrac{50}{110}$

$= 0.4545454$

Angle a = 63·0°

TOA

$\tan b° = \dfrac{opp}{adj}$

$= \dfrac{75}{120}$

$= 0.625$

Angle b = 32·0°

SOH

$\sin c° = \dfrac{opp}{hyp}$

$= \dfrac{23}{45}$

$= 0.5111111$

Angle c = 30·7°

1 ▶ Do Worksheet 7, question 2.

2 Find the size of each marked angle correct to 1 dp.

(a)

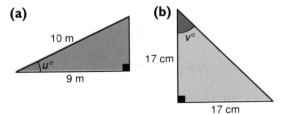

(b)

(c)

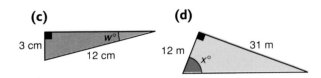

(d)

(e)

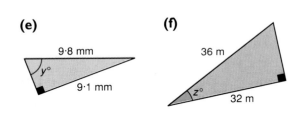

(f)

3 Find the angle, $b°$ of the roof in the playhouse.

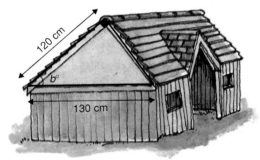

4 The sketch shows the scrambling net in the toddler's park. One side is vertical. Find the angle, $c°$, the support makes with the ground.

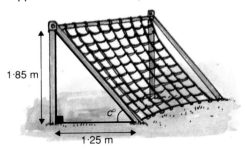

When the sun's rays make an angle of 55° to the ground this flagpole casts a shadow 3·8 m long.

To calculate the height of the flagpole:

$$\tan 55° = \frac{opp}{adj}$$

T O A

$$\tan 55° = \frac{h}{3·8}$$

$$1·428 = \frac{h}{3·8}$$

$$1·428 \times 3·8 = h$$

$$h = 5·4264$$

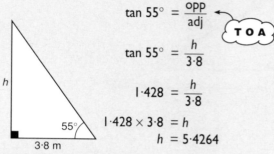

The height of the flagpole is **5·4 m**, correct to 1 decimal place.

1 ▶ Do Worksheet 8, question 1.

2 Find the height of each flagpole.

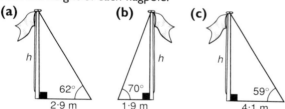

(a) 62° 2·9 m **(b)** 70° 1·9 m **(c)** 59° 4·1 m

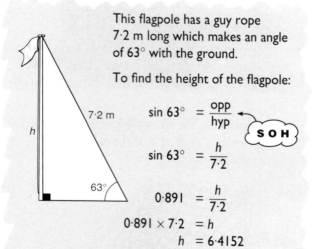

This flagpole has a guy rope 7·2 m long which makes an angle of 63° with the ground.

To find the height of the flagpole:

$$\sin 63° = \frac{opp}{hyp}$$

S O H

$$\sin 63° = \frac{h}{7·2}$$

$$0·891 = \frac{h}{7·2}$$

$$0·891 \times 7·2 = h$$

$$h = 6·4152$$

The height of the flagpole is **6·4 m**, correct to 1 decimal place.

3 ▶ Do Worksheet 8, question 2.

4 Find the height of each flagpole.

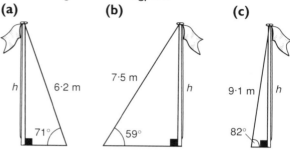

(a) h 6·2 m 71° **(b)** 7·5 m h 59° **(c)** 9·1 m h 82°

This flagpole has a guy rope 5·3 m long which makes an angle of 72° with the ground.
To find the distance between the bottom of the guy rope and the foot of the flagpole:

$$\cos 72° = \frac{adj}{hyp}$$

C A H

$$\cos 72° = \frac{d}{5·3}$$

$$0·309 = \frac{d}{5·3}$$

$$0·309 \times 5·3 = d$$

$$d = 1·6377$$

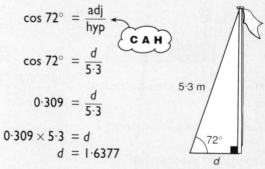

5·3 m 72° d

The distance is **1·6 m**, correct to 1 decimal place.

5 ▶ Do Worksheet 8, question 3.

6 Find the distance between the bottom of the guy rope and the foot of the flagpole.

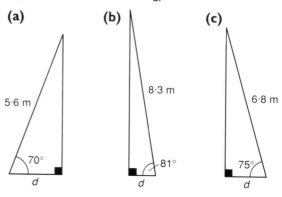

(a) 5·6 m 70° d **(b)** 8·3 m 81° d **(c)** 6·8 m 75° d

7 ▶ Do Worksheet 8, question 4.

8 In each triangle find the length of the marked side.

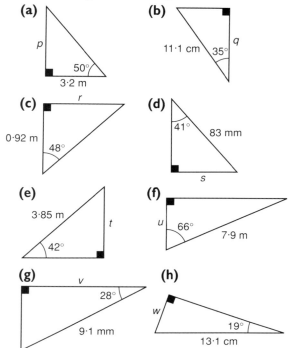

(a)

p
50°
3·2 m

(b)

11·1 cm   35° q

(c)

r
0·92 m   48°

(d)

41°   83 mm
s

(e)

3·85 m t
42°

(f)

u 66°
7·9 m

(g)

v 28°
9·1 mm

(h)

w 19°
13·1 cm

9 Find the length of the side marked x on this 60° set square.

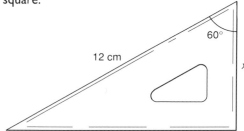

60°
12 cm
x

10 An aircraft is descending at an angle of 13°. When its horizontal distance from the runway marker is 3000 m, how high above the ground is the aircraft?

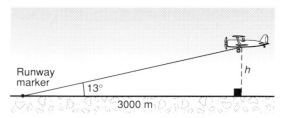

Runway marker
13°
3000 m
h

11 A 2 m ladder is resting against a wall. The angle between the wall and the ladder is 28°.

(a) Make a sketch.

(b) How far up the wall does the ladder reach?

12 Find the length, l, of the upright on the metal bracket.

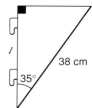

l
38 cm
35°

13 Find the height of the tower.

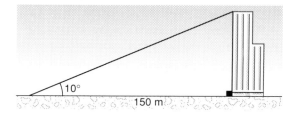

10°
150 m

14 In triangle PQR, $\widehat{PRQ} = 90°$, $\widehat{PQR} = 32°$ and PQ = 6 cm.

(a) Sketch triangle PQR marking in angles and the length of side PQ.

(b) Calculate the length of PR.

15 From the diagram what is the height of the taller flagpole?

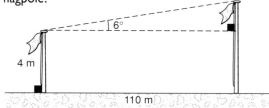

6°
4 m
110 m

16 This windsock pole is held in position by four wire guy ropes of equal length. The total length of wire used is 100 m. The angle between each guy and the ground is 73°.

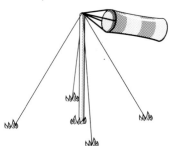

(a) Sketch the right-angled triangle formed by the windsock pole, a guy rope and the ground.

(b) Find the height of the pole.

Figure it out

1 From a boat, 1500 feet out to sea, the angle of elevation of this cliff is 13°.
How high is the cliff?

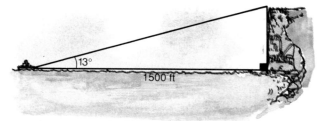

13°
1500 ft

2 A 90 cm fence post casts a shadow 68 cm long.
Find the angle the sun's rays make with the ground.

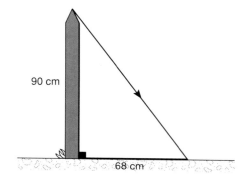

90 cm
68 cm

3 A 1·7 m plank is resting against a wall at an angle of 72° to the ground.
(a) Make a sketch.
(b) How far is the foot of the plank from the wall?

4 The guy rope for this tent pole is 2·1 m long.
The tent pole is 1·3 m high.
What is the angle between the guy rope and the ground?

5 A ship sails 35 km due west from port. It changes course and sails on a bearing of 065° until it is due north of its starting point.
(a) Sketch the course of the ship.
(b) Calculate how far the ship is from port.

6 The 5·2 m guy rope to a flagpole is at an angle of 42° to the ground.
What is the height of the flagpole?

7 The handle on the garden roller is 1·3 m long.
The roller has a radius of 12 cm.

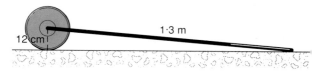

12 cm
1·3 m

What angle does the handle make with the ground?

8 The longest side of a 45° set square is 10 cm.
What are the lengths of the other two sides?

9 For each set of points:
• plot the points and join them to form a triangle
• find the size of $P\widehat{Q}R$.
(a) P($^-2, 2$), Q($^-2, ^-1$), R($4, 2$)
(b) P($5, ^-3$), Q($5, 6$), R($8, ^-3$)

10 Chas is designing a climbing wall.
Find the size of angle $a°$.

5 m
$a°$
1 m
climbing wall

▶ Challenge

11 Greta walks 2 miles due east, then 3 miles due north.
(a) Sketch Greta's route.
(b) If Greta had gone in a straight line from start to finish, how far and on what bearing would she have walked?

The heights, to the nearest inch, of students in class 5C are shown in the frequency table.

The **cumulative frequency** column gives a running total.

Height (inches)	Frequency	Cumulative frequency
63	2	2
64	5	7
65	7	14
66	10	24
67	4	28
68	2	30

add
add

28 pupils are 67 inches tall or less

The table is used to draw a **cumulative frequency curve**.

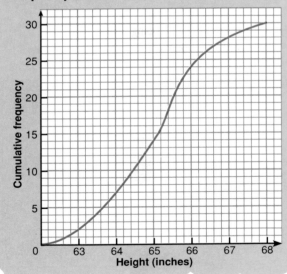

1 Use the table to find the number of students who are:

(a) 64 inches or less

(b) 66 inches or less.

2 Use the curve to estimate the number of students who are:

(a) $65\frac{1}{2}$ inches or less

(b) $66\frac{1}{2}$ inches or less.

▶ **You need Worksheets 9 and 10.**

3 (a) Complete Cumulative Frequency Table 1.
   (b) Complete Cumulative Frequency Curve 1.
   (c) How many students weigh 53 kg or less?
   (d) Estimate the number of students weighing 55·5 kg or less.

4 (a) Complete Table 2.
   (b) Complete Curve 2, using the **upper limit** of each class interval.
   (c) How many students scored 50 or less?
   (d) If the pass mark is 35, estimate how many students failed.

5 (a) For class 5C's French marks complete Table 3.

5	11	21	16	8	27	42
46	39	7	17	29	39	48
19	22	21	32	15	46	25
19	8	33	41	38	36	9
26	21	49	35	29	35	27

   (b) Complete Curve 3.
   (c) Estimate how many students scored 25 or less.

6 In a science experiment class 5C measured their reaction times in seconds.

1·8	1·7	2·1	1·4	1·4	1·5	2·6
2·0	1·7	0·9	3·0	1·7	1·2	1·3
0·8	2·5	2·5	2·7	2·4	1·8	1·4
1·7	1·5	1·5	2·4	2·1	1·2	1·2
3·4	3·1	2·9	2·5	2·5	2·6	1·9

   (a) Complete Table 4.
   (b) Complete Curve 4.
   (c) How many students have a reaction time of:
   • 1 second or less
   • 2 seconds or less?
   (d) Estimate how many students have a reaction time **greater** than 2·85 seconds.

Keeping them in order

The **range** of a set of data is the difference between the largest and smallest values.

5 7 |4| 11 |12| 9 9 10 12 5 8

$$\text{Range} = 12 - 4$$
$$= 8$$

The **median** is the middle value when the data are **arranged in order**.

4 5 5 7 8 |9| 9 10 11 12 12

↑
Median

7 7 7 11 12 |□| 15 16 18 18 21

↑
Median
13·5

The **upper quartile** and **lower quartile** are the middle values of the upper and lower halves of the data.

Lower half   Upper half

4 5 |5| 7 8 |9| 9 10 |11| 12 12

↑   ↑   ↑
Lower quartile Median Upper quartile

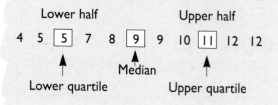

12 14 |□| 14 16 |□| 18 22 |□| 23 25

↑   ↑   ↑
Lower quartile Median Upper quartile
14   17   22·5

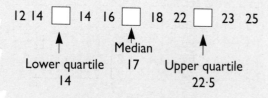

Inter-quartile = upper quartile − lower quartile
range   = 22·5   − 14
                = 8·5

1 For each set of data:
  • arrange the figures in order
  • find the median
  • find the upper and lower quartiles
  • calculate the inter-quartile range.

(a) 6 7 4 5 3 8 9 9 13 15 4
(b) 21 24 30 23 18 12 31 23 27
(c) 3 5 6 2 3 7 9 11 12 6
(d) 3 7 12 32 12 45 56 32

Mrs Seagrave has made a cumulative frequency table for 5C's maths grades.
There are 7 grades for 31 students.

Grade	Frequency	Cumulative frequency
1	2	2
2	5	7
3	5	12
4	7	19
5	4	23
6	7	30
7	1	31

Lower quartile → 2
Median → 3
→ 4
Upper quartile → 6

8th value
8th value → 12
16th value → 19
16th value → 23
24th value → 30

15 students   16th Median   15 students

7 students 8th 7 students 7 students 24th 7 students
Lower quartile   Upper quartile
Inter-quartile range

Inter-quartile range = 6 − 3
                     = 3

2 From each cumulative frequency table find:
  • the median   • the upper and lower quartiles
  • the inter-quartile range.

(a)

Mark	Frequency	Cum. frequency
21	4	4
22	2	6
23	5	11
24	1	12
25	5	17
26	8	25
27	6	31

(b)

Score	Frequency	Cum. frequency
7	1	1
8	3	4
9	4	8
10	11	19
11	9	28
12	7	35
13	4	39

This is a cumulative frequency curve for the grades of all 199 students in year 11.
Mrs Seagrave uses it to find the median, the quartiles and the inter-quartile range.

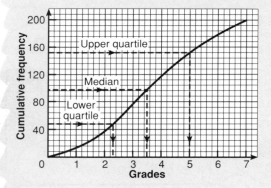

The total number of students is 199

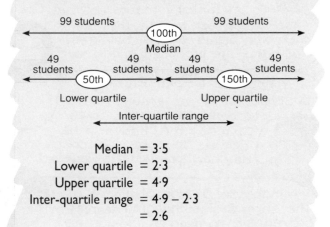

Median = 3·5
Lower quartile = 2·3
Upper quartile = 4·9
Inter-quartile range = 4·9 − 2·3
= 2·6

3 From each cumulative frequency curve estimate:
• the median
• the upper and lower quartiles
• the inter-quartile range.

(a)

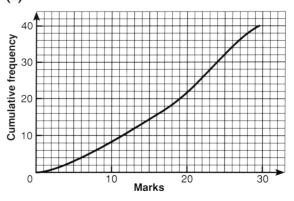

(b)

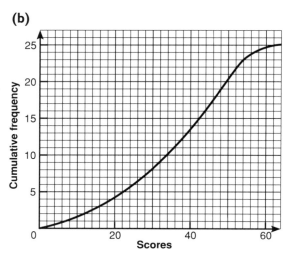

Ka Yi and Euan are on work experience at Radio Dunedin.
They join Ross Brady's *Early Bird Show*.
Ross shows them his programme schedule.

Early Bird Show
6.05 Wake up to Ross Brady.
Travel Information: 6.15, 6.35, 6.55, 7.15, 7.35, 7.55, 8.15, 8.35, 8.55.
News : On the hour.
Headlines : On the half hour.
Morning Thought: 6.40, 7.40, 8.40
Finish: 9.00

....and Ka Yi and Euan will be putting today's Mindbender questions.

1 The *Early Bird Show* finishes at 9 am.
(a) How long does the show last?
(b) News headlines last three minutes. How much time is spent on headlines?
(c) What percentage of the show is spent on travel information, if each travel bulletin lasts two minutes?

2 At 8.20 Ross has a phone-in slot. 240 people phoned the station, but only 8 spoke to Ross on air. What was the probability of a caller getting on air?

3 Between 6.35 and 6.55 Ross plays three records lasting 3 min 15 sec, 3 min 42 sec and 2 min 58 sec respectively. If the *Morning Thought* lasts 4 minutes, how much time does Ross fill by talking?

4 The show goes out on FM and can be picked up on a frequency of 96.5 ± 0.8 MHz. Between which two frequencies can listeners tune in?

5 Solve the five Mindbenders read by Ka Yi and Euan.

Mindbender 1 : In and Around.
A square and a rectangle have the same area. The rectangle has length 4 cm and breadth 16 cm. What is the perimeter of the square?

Mindbender 2 : Ages and Ages
Tom is 28 and Perry is 6. How old will Perry be when he is half Tom's age?

Mindbender 3: Boxed In.
A factory makes bolts at the rate of 136 per minute. They are packed in boxes of 140. How many full boxes are produced in one hour?

Mindbender 4: Self Raising.
A school cook has enough flour to make 180 sponge cakes each day for 9 days. If he decides to make 270 cakes a day, how long will the flour last?

Mindbender 5: Hot Stuff.
The formula for changing degrees Fahrenheit to degrees Celsius is
$$C = \frac{5(F - 32)}{9}$$
Change 77°F to degrees C.

Ka Yi and Euan spend a day with Sammy, the Programme Director.

They look at the evening programme chart for the week.

Radio Dunedin – Evening programmes

	Saturday	Sunday		Monday		Tuesday		Wednesday		Thursday		Friday	
6 pm	Play the Game	Feelin' Blue		News		News		News		News		News	
				On the Line		The Green Machine		Mainstream		Techno Babble		Wheeling & Dealing	
				The Bottom Line									
7 pm	Back Chat	Open University	Black on White	Trading Places	All of a Quaver	Holding Forth	Celtic Links	Holding Forth	Under Wraps	Holding Forth	On Tour	Speaking out	Toeing the Line
				Note Book									
8 pm	On Tour			Jean Nichols		Jean Nichols		Jean Nichols		Jean Nichols		Jean Nichols	
9 pm				Snap Shots	Gaelic	Snap Shots	Gaelic	Snap Shots	Gaelic	Snap Shots	Gaelic	Snap Shots	Gaelic
10 pm	News	News		News		News		News		News		News	
	Celtic Links	Under Wraps		Freewheeling		Freewheeling		Freewheeling		Freewheeling		Freewheeling	

Waveband

both FM and MW

FM only

MW only

6 How long do the following programmes last?

(a) *All of a Quaver*   (b) *News*

(c) *Note Book*   (d) *Open University*

7 (a) On which waveband, *FM* or *MW*, are Gaelic programmes broadcast?

(b) On which night of the week are all programmes on both FM and MW?

8 (a) *Play the Game* covers events from Britain and the rest of Europe in the ratio 7 : 3. How much time is spent on British events?

(b) Each weekday evening the ratio of time for broadcasts on **FM only** to broadcasts on **FM and MW** is the same. What is this ratio?

(c) On a Wednesday evening, what percentage of time is spent on news broadcasts?

9 Sammy wants to reduce the length of the Open University broadcast by 15%. How long would the programme last?

10 Sammy showed Ka Yi the results of a listeners' survey.

(a) 13 out of 25 said they tune in to only *MW* programmes. Write this as a percentage.

(b) $\frac{5}{12}$ of listeners leave their radios tuned to just one station and $\frac{1}{4}$ tune to only two stations.

The rest tune to more than two stations. What fraction tune to more than two stations?

11 In Sammy's department the staff are allocated as follows:

11 to News, 7 to Production,

8 to Current Affairs and 4 to Library.

(a) Draw a pie chart to show this allocation of staff.

(b) This pie chart shows the breakdown of their wages.

Compare the staff pie chart with the wages pie chart. Which staff do you think have the highest rates of pay? Explain.

Wages

Ka Yi and Euan are introduced to Petra Sellars, the Advertising Manager.
The radio station makes commercials and sells airtime.
Ka Yi and Euan watch the commercials being recorded.

The tables show:
• the basic cost of making a radio advertisement using one voice
• the cost of optional extras.

Basic Cost

Length of commercial (seconds)	Cost (£)
10	50
20 or 30	60
40 or 50	70
60	80

Optional Extras

Extras	Cost (£)
Additional voice	25
Background music	55
Jingle	800
Sound effects	15

I How much would Petra charge for each commercial?

Company	Length (s)	Extras
Mental Motors	20	None
Freezar Meats	10	Additional voice and Background music
Barrs Self Drive	40	Jingle
Simpson's Furnishing	30	Two Sound effects and Additional voice

2 Radio Dunedin reaches 56·5% of the population who live within range of their transmitters. If the population of the area is 906 000, how many people listen to Radio Dunedin?

3 Find the total cost of each item advertised on Radio Dunedin. Assume the rate of VAT is 17·5%.

(a)

Simpson's Furnishing 3 piece suites for ONLY £999. Price is exclusive of VAT.

(b)

Second hand cars. Cheapest in town from Mental Motors. 'H' registered Rover 216 SLi ONLY £7145, excluding VAT.

(c)

Now! A better deal from... Barrs Self Drive Vans. Hire a Transit for only £55 per day, VAT not included.

This table gives the cost in £'s of airtime for advertising.

Time of broadcast	Length of commercial in seconds					
	10	20	30	40	50	60
0600–1200	45	72	90	117	148	162
1200–1800	19	30	38	49	62	68
1800–2400	9	14	18	23	29	32
2400–0600	2	3	4	5	6	7

4 Find the cost of airtime for each commercial.

   (a) Simpson's Furnishing, 40 seconds at 1500
   (b) King's Hall Concerts, 20 seconds at 1130
   (c) Marx and Engels Store, 30 seconds at 0715
   (d) Cheapo Muzac, 10 seconds at 11.23 pm
   (e) Flix Cinema, 20 seconds at 5.05 pm
   (f) Fair Cabs, 30 seconds at 9.20 pm

5 Marx and Engels have recently opened a new store. They want to broadcast a 30 second commercial once every 2 hours. The first commercial goes on air at 0720 and the last at 2320. Find the total cost of their airtime for one day.

6 (a) Between which times do you think broadcasts attract: • most listeners • fewest listeners? Explain your answers.

   (b) Look at the cost of advertising between 2400 and 0600. Using *c* for the cost in £'s and *t* for the time in seconds, write a formula linking *c* and *t*.

7 Imran, the manager of Star Stores, is considering advertising on Radio Dunedin. In a special promotion, airtime is being offered at two different rates.

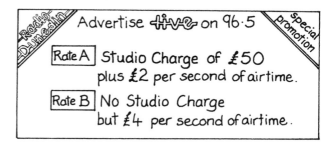

Ka Yi and Euan are calculating the costs for Imran.
(a) Copy and complete each table.

Rate A

Time (s)	10	20	30	40	50	60
Cost (£)	70					

Rate B

Time (s)	10	20	30	40	50	60
Cost (£)	40					

You need 2 mm graph paper.

(b) On the same diagram draw graphs to show the cost at each rate.
(c) What advice should Ka Yi and Euan give to Imran?

This is the area served by Radio Dunedin. Each morning Jenny broadcasts road traffic reports from a helicopter. The route taken by the helicopter is shown on the map.

Key
(H) Heliport
(F) Forth Road Bridge
(N) Newbridge roundabout
(S) Sherrifhall roundabout
(M) Musselburgh
Scale 1 : 250 000

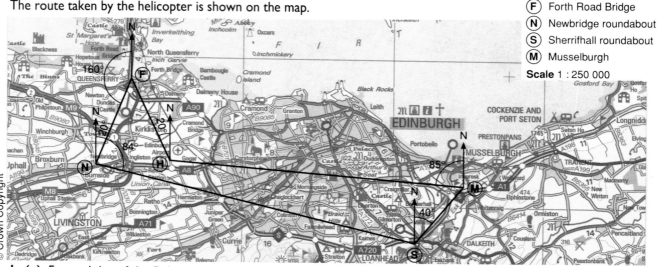

1 (a) For each leg of the flight:
  • find the bearing
  • calculate the distance travelled, in km.
(b) Find the total distance travelled.
(c) The flight time is 90 minutes. Calculate the average speed of the helicopter.

2

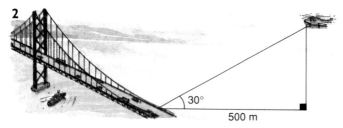

The helicopter is hovering 500 m from the Forth Road Bridge. From the road the angle of elevation of the helicopter is 30°.
Use a scale drawing to find the height of the helicopter above the road.

3 Jenny spots Craighall roundabout at an angle of depression of 20°. The altimeter indicates a height of 225 m. What is the horizontal distance from the helicopter to the roundabout?

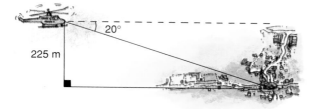

4 This graph shows the amount of fuel used by the helicopter.

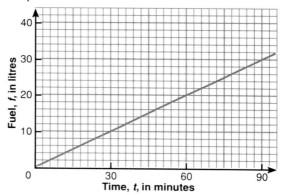

(a) How many litres of fuel are used if the helicopter is in the air for 90 minutes?
(b) How long could the helicopter stay in the air if it had 20 litres of fuel?
(c) Write a formula connecting the fuel used and the flight time.

5 As he approaches the Newbridge roundabout, John hears Jenny's 7.55 am report: 'Due to an accident at the Newbridge roundabout, drivers heading for Edinburgh can expect delays of up to 1 hour 20 min.' John usually takes 25 minutes to travel from Newbridge to work.

(a) When can he expect to arrive?
(b) He still has 15 miles to travel when he hears the report. Find his expected average speed for this part of his journey.

Radio Dunedin is running an appeal for famine relief. Ka Yi and Euan go with Stevie and the outside broadcast team to Thor's Challenge.

1 For Thor's Challenge Ka Yi paid £15 for three adult and two children's tickets. Euan paid £9·50 for two adults and one child. What are the ticket prices?

2 In Odin's Race each challenger is timed over one lap of the track.

  (a) Find the length of the track.

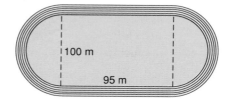

  (b) The fastest time is 1 min 30 sec. Find the speed of the winner in m/s.

3 There are two ramps for the Winged Helmet event, one for adults and one for children.

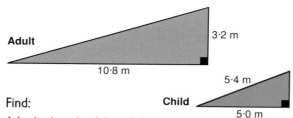

Find:

(a) the length of the adult ramp

(b) the height of the child's ramp.

4 At the Nordic Quiver event the leading challenger scored 150 with five arrows. Find all possible ways of making this score.

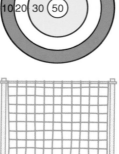

5 For the Raiders event, challengers have to climb a 5·3 m net made of ropes intertwined at 30 cm intervals. One challenger has an average step of 70 cm with his left leg and 90 cm with his right. If he starts with his right leg, how many steps does he take to get one foot over the top of the net?

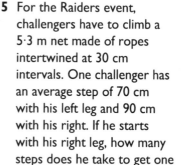

6 In the Fire Fighters event, each challenger must carry two buckets of water across a beam.

  (a) Calculate the volume of each cylindrical bucket.

  (b) Find the minimum number of return trips required to fill a 200 litre tank.

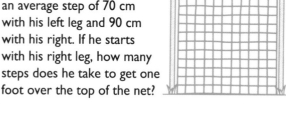

More problems

1 Ian is pegging out the ropes for his runner beans. He uses 15 m of rope cut into 8 equal lengths. The pole is 1·8 m high. Find the angle between each rope and the ground.

2 For medical reasons Greta walks two miles every day. She walks at an average speed of 3 mph. Over a two-week period, how long does she spend walking?

3 Mr Strang has collected Class 5Y's maths marks.

```
35   18   31    5   37   22   31   40
26   17   21   19   28   22   37   39
19   21   31   33   25   25   29   32
26   30   30   38   17   10   19   31
```

If 25% of the class pass the test, find the pass mark.

4 To calculate the number of teachers needed for each school, an education authority use the formula
$$t = 0.0596p + 10.25$$
where t is the number of teachers and
p is the number of pupils.

(a) Clyde High School has 532 pupils. How many teachers should it have?

(b) Strangehill has 830 pupils and 58 teachers. Is the school staffed at the correct level?

(c) Eleanor wants to use a graph to calculate the number of teachers for each school. Which graph should she use?

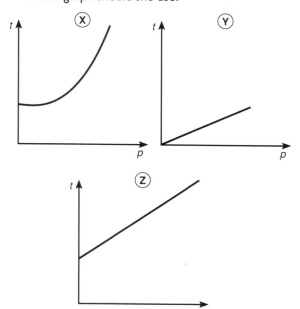

5 On a $9\frac{1}{2}$ hour flight from Los Angeles to London, the entertainments guide shows this diagram for the programme of films.

Programme A	Programme B	Programme C
2h 15 min	2h 15 min	2h 15 min

There is a 15 minute intermission between programmes.

◆ Programme A starts 45 mins after take-off.
◆ Los Angeles is 8 hours behind London.
◆ The plane took off at 1810 LA time.
Use the information above to find when Programme C begins, London time.

6 To settle a dispute between neighbours, it is agreed that trees along the dividing fence should be no taller than 25 feet.

Will this tree have to be cut back? Explain.

1m = 3·28 feet

22°

20 m

7 In France, new drivers are restricted to a maximum speed of 90 km/h for one year. Jean Paul drove from Paris to Calais, a distance of 295 km, in 3h 45 mins. He stopped for 35 minutes for lunch on the way. Did he exceed the new driver's limit? Explain.

8 A farmer left her flock of
sheep to her daughters.
Rachel received half the flock,
Liz one third and Eva the
rest. Eva received 24 sheep.
What size was the farmer's
flock?

9 In an earthquake zone in India, normal house building
techniques are adapted to make houses earthquake
proof.

Wooden frames
like this

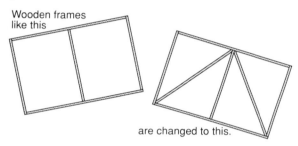

are changed to this.

(a) Find the extra length of wood required to adapt
this frame in the same way.

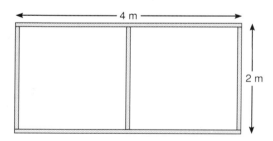

(b) Each wall of this new house is to have an
earthquake-proof wooden frame. Ignoring doors
and windows, find the total length of timber
required for the four walls.

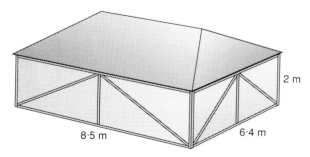

10

Input → Multiply by 3 → Subtract 8 → Output

Use the number machine to find:

(a) the output when the input is 6
(b) the input if the output is 7
(c) the number which is unchanged by the
machine.

11 (a) Write an expression for the perimeter of this
shape.

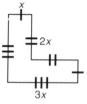

(b) Find the perimeter when $x = 3$ cm.
(c) A similar shape has area 180 cm². What is the
value of x for this shape?

12 At the school fête, Jason has set up a game.
Competitors roll three balls towards the holes.
Each ball falling through a numbered hole counts
towards the total score.

(a) How many ways are there of scoring 11?
(b) Every teddy costs Jason £3·50.
For every winner, how many people must lose
for Jason to make a profit?
(c) Jason calculates the probability of winning is $\frac{1}{9}$.
What is his expected profit after 90 games?

▶ **You need Worksheets 11, 12 and 13, a ruler, a pair of compasses and a protractor.**

1   When Fred, the window cleaner, is standing half-way up the ladder, the ladder slides slowly down the wall, to the ground.

On Diagram 1
■ For each position of the ladder, mark Fred's position with a cross.
■ Join the points with a smooth curve to show the path of Fred's descent.

2   Bruce starts water-skiing directly behind a boat and then swings out to his right. The boat is travelling at 10 metres per second and Bruce swings out 10° every second.

On Diagram 2
■ Mark with a cross Bruce's position after each second.
■ Join the points with a smooth curve to show the path of Bruce's course.

3   Costa is rowing across the river towards the landing stage. The current is pushing his boat downstream. For every 10 m Costa rows towards the landing stage, the current takes his boat 5 m further down river.

On Diagram 3
■ Mark Costa's position after every 10 m he rows.
■ Join the points with a smooth curve to show the locus of the boat.

4   A gazelle runs at 20 m/s in a straight line past a concealed cheetah. The cheetah starts chasing it at 30 m/s. The cheetah always runs directly towards the gazelle.

On Diagram 4
■ Mark the cheetah's position each second after the start of the chase.
■ Draw the locus of the cheetah.

5   Hayley walks from the centre of the carousel towards the edge. For each metre she walks, the carousel rotates through 20°

On Diagram 5
■ Mark Hayley's position every metre until she reaches the edge.
■ Draw her locus.

6 Dobbin is tethered by a 15 metre rope to a peg.

On **Diagram 6** complete the scale drawing and shade the area of grass **within** Dobbin's reach.

7 Spot is a guard dog. At night he is kept on a 10 metre chain which is attached to the middle of the back wall of the house.

On **Diagram 7** complete the scale drawing and shade the area of the garden **outside** Spot's reach.

8 There are floodlights along the fence at HM Prison Dungrabbin. Each light illuminates a circle on the ground with radius 10 m. A strip of ground 8 m wide has to be lit on both sides of the fence.

On **Diagram 8** complete the scale drawing to find the positions of the minimum number of lights which will illuminate the required area.

The **area** formed by a set of points is also called a **locus**.

9 One-eyed Jim's treasure is buried within 5 metres of the Oak Tree, within 6 metres of Pulpit Rock and within 4 metres of Nectar Spring.

On **Diagram 9** complete the scale drawing and shade the locus of Jim's treasure.

10 Paddy plugs his electric mower into a socket which is 1 m along from the corner of his hut. The mower is fitted with a 5 m extension cable. The hut is 4 m long and 3 m wide.

On **Diagram 10** complete the scale drawing and shade the locus of Paddy's mower.

- Use the code to decipher the clue for each number.
- Use the formula to find the mystery number.
- Check that you have the right answer.

Code

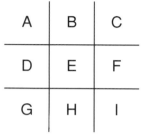  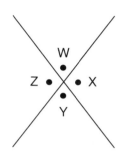

Clue: First number: *a*

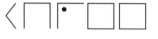  

Clue: Second number: *b*

 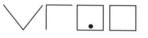 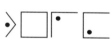

Clue: Third number: *c*

 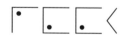 

Clue: Fourth number: *d*

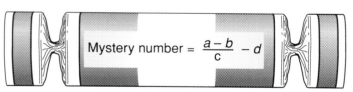

Formula

Mystery number $= \dfrac{a - b}{c} - d$

Check your answer

Gwen and Mervyn tie ribbon round identical gift boxes. They both begin with the same length of ribbon.

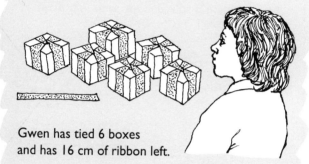

Gwen has tied 6 boxes and has 16 cm of ribbon left.

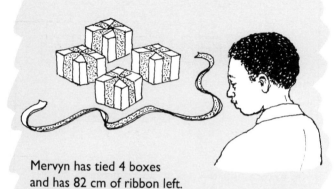

Mervyn has tied 4 boxes and has 82 cm of ribbon left.

If r is the length of ribbon in cm round each box, then

$$6r + 16 = 4r + 82$$

$-4r$ $-4r$

$$2r + 16 = 82$$

-16 -16

$$2r = 66$$

$\div 2$ $\div 2$

$$r = 33$$

There is **33 cm** of ribbon round each box.

1 Gwen and Mervyn start with the same length of ribbon and tie these boxes. Form an equation and solve it to find the length of ribbon needed for one box.

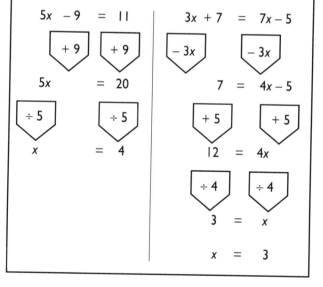

● **Remember**
- In an equation the letter stands for an unknown number.
- Solving an equation means finding the value of the unknown number.
- Keep the equation balanced by doing the same to both sides.

$$5x - 9 = 11$$

$+ 9$ $+ 9$

$$5x = 20$$

$\div 5$ $\div 5$

$$x = 4$$

$$3x + 7 = 7x - 5$$

$- 3x$ $- 3x$

$$7 = 4x - 5$$

$+ 5$ $+ 5$

$$12 = 4x$$

$\div 4$ $\div 4$

$$3 = x$$

$$x = 3$$

---

2 Solve:

(a) $3x + 2 = 11$ (b) $7r + 3 = 52$

(c) $8 + 4q = 28$ (d) $9 + 5t = 44$

(e) $12v + 6 = 42$ (f) $2p - 4 = 36$

(g) $5q + 1 = 3q + 7$ (h) $6y + 1 = 2y + 17$

(i) $9i - 5 = 6i + 13$ (j) $4t - 20 = t + 1$

(k) $5h + 3 = 8h - 12$ (l) $12v + 5 = 5 - v$

(m) $9d + 8 = 4d + 48$ (n) $7 - 3c = c - 1$

In the balance

Gwen has made up a pack of 5 identical gift boxes to be posted. The scales show that the pack weighs more than 2000 grams.

If w is the weight of one box in grams

$$5w > 2000$$

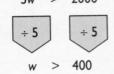

$$w > 400$$

Each box weighs **more than 400 grams**.

1 The scales show that Mervyn's pack of 3 identical novelty boxes weighs more than 150 grams.

Write an inequation, solve it and make a statement about the weight of each box.

2 This pack of 4 identical display boxes weighs less than 1000 grams.

Write an inequation, solve it and make a statement about the weight of each box.

3 A pack of 8 identical variety boxes weighs more than 2400 grams. Write an inequation, solve it and make a statement about the weight of each box.

4 A pack of 12 identical gift boxes weighs less than 480 grams. Write an inequation, solve it and make a statement about the weight of each box.

● Remember
- In an inequation the letter represents a **set** of unknown numbers.
- An inequation is solved in the same way as an equation.

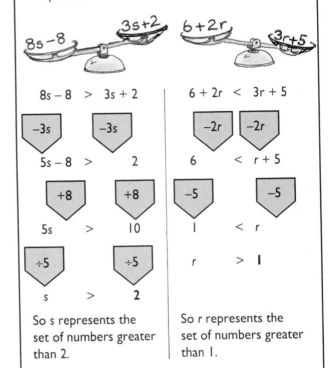

$$8s - 8 > 3s + 2 \qquad 6 + 2r < 3r + 5$$

$-3s \qquad -3s \qquad\qquad -2r \qquad -2r$

$$5s - 8 > 2 \qquad\qquad 6 < r + 5$$

$+8 \qquad +8 \qquad\qquad -5 \qquad\qquad -5$

$$5s > 10 \qquad\qquad 1 < r$$

$÷5 \qquad ÷5 \qquad\qquad r > 1$

$$s > 2$$

So s represents the set of numbers greater than 2.

So r represents the set of numbers greater than 1.

5 Solve each inequation:

(a) $5a + 4 > 24$

(b) $2 + f < 18$

(c) $7 + 4c \leqslant 39$

(d) $29 \geqslant 7x + 1$

(e) $49 > 5 + 11y$

(f) $15g + 6 < 51$

(g) $20x + 9 \geqslant 49$

(h) $17 < 1 + 8t$

(i) $9d + 4 < 22 + 7d$

(j) $10 + 7b \leqslant 8b + 7$

(k) $13 + 3n < 1 + 7n$

(l) $9d + 4 < 22 + 7d$

(m) $10x < 9 + x$

(n) $20 + 5w \geqslant 9w + 4$

(o) $6p - 5 > 13$

(p) $1 \leqslant 5w - 4$

6 Gwen weighs identical novelty boxes. Five boxes plus 100 grams is heavier than three boxes plus 300 grams. Write an inequation, solve it and make a statement about the weight of each box.

7 Mervyn weighs identical bargain boxes. Nine boxes plus 200 grams weigh less than 6 boxes plus 800 grams. Write an inequation, solve it and make a statement about the weight of each box.

Rob sells Christmas hampers.
Each hamper contains 3 bottles
of wine and 2 cakes.
If the cost in pounds of
1 bottle of wine is w and
of 1 cake is c then the cost
of this hamper is $3w + 2c$.

The cost in pounds of 5 of these hampers is

$3w + 2c + 3w + 2c + 3w + 2c + 3w + 2c + 3w + 2c$
$= 3w + 3w + 3w + 3w + 3w + 2c + 2c + 2c + 2c + 2c$
$= 15w + 10c$

or $5(3w + 2c) = 5 \times 3w + 5 \times 2c = 15w + 10c$

1 Write an expression using brackets for the cost of 3 of Rob's Christmas hampers.

● **Remember**

$4(3d + 7) = 12d + 28$ $6(4s - 3) = 24s - 18$

---

2 Multiply out:

(a) $3(4b + 2)$ (b) $7(3k + 9)$ (c) $6(5a - 8)$
(d) $2(12 + v)$ (e) $9(9 - 2k)$ (f) $5(13x + 7)$
(g) $12(8 - 7p)$ (h) $7(6f + 13)$ (i) $7(4 - 9f)$

You can solve equations containing brackets by
first multiplying out the bracket.

$4p = 2(3 - p)$
$4p = 6 - 2p$

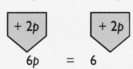

$6p = 6$

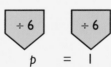

$p = 1$

3 Solve each equation:

(a) $3(2w + 1) = 21$ (b) $5(9 + 3x) = 75$
(c) $56 = 2(3 + 5y)$ (d) $63 = 7(f + 5)$
(e) $6(7a - 1) = 36$ (f) $5(4g - 5) = 35$
(g) $10 = 5(8 - p)$ (h) $8 = 8(2r - 3)$
(i) $4(6 + 5x) = 224$ (j) $10(3b - 4) = 50$

(k) $36 = 3(12 + 2c)$ (l) $76 = 2(3b - 7)$
(m) $4(f + 1) = 4$ (n) $6(2w - 4) = 0$
(o) $2(y + 1) = 8$ (p) $4(7 - 3m) = 2m$

Some equations also contain fractions.

$\frac{1}{3} b$ can be written as $\frac{b}{3}$

$\frac{2}{7} c$ can be written as $\frac{2c}{7}$

When solving equations with fractions first make
the fractions into whole numbers by multiplying.

$\frac{2}{5} b = 4$ $\frac{3y}{7} - 3 = 6$

$2b = 20$ $3y - 21 = 42$

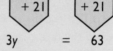

$b = 10$ $3y = 63$

$y = 21$

4 Solve each equation.

(a) $\frac{1}{2}x = 5$ (b) $9 = \frac{1}{4}y$
(c) $\frac{k}{3} = 10$ (d) $7 = \frac{a}{5}$
(e) $\frac{1}{7}p = 8$ (f) $\frac{r}{9} = 11$
(g) $4 = \frac{2}{3}b$ (h) $\frac{5h}{6} = 10$
(i) $\frac{3}{8}g = 6$ (j) $18 = \frac{9g}{10}$
(k) $\frac{1}{4}t + 5 = 7$ (l) $5 = \frac{1}{2}w - 3$
(m) $\frac{1}{8}v - 7 = 1$ (n) $9 = 4 + \frac{b}{10}$
(o) $\frac{4}{5}b + 2 = 10$ (p) $\frac{3m}{8} - 2 = 1$
(q) $\frac{7}{10}y + 12 = 68$ (r) $\frac{3k}{2} - 5 = 13$

▼ **Challenge**

5 Solve each equation.

(a) $\frac{21}{w} = 7$ (b) $\frac{39}{d} = 3$ (c) $\frac{48}{f} = 6$
(d) $\frac{56}{u} = 7$ (e) $\frac{81}{h} = 9$ (f) $\frac{18}{d} = 6$

Under Raps

Blair hires out karaoke machines. He uses these formulae to help him work out costs, wages and hire charges.

$C = H + 9$ Subject is C
$H = 6T$ Subject is H
$W = 15T$ Subject is W

When formulae are written like this, the first letter is known as the **subject**.

1 Write the subject of each formula.
  (a) $C = H + 4$ **(b)** $V = IR$
  (c) $D = ST$ **(d)** $p = i^2 r$

2 Blair uses $C = H + 9$ to calculate the total cost for a karaoke machine, where C is the total cost and H is the hire charge in £.
  (a) Find the total cost when the hire charge is:
      • £17 • £48 • £27 • £35 • £162
  (b) Find the hire charge when the total cost is:
      • £25 • £19 • £77 • £46 • £153

The subject of the formula $C = H + 4$ is C.
The formula can be rearranged to make H the subject.

$$C \quad = H + 4$$

$$\boxed{-4} \quad \boxed{-4}$$

$$C - 4 = H$$
$$H = C - 4$$

3 Use the formula $H = C - 4$ to find the hire charge, H, when the total cost, C, is:
  (a) £63   **(b)** £21   **(c)** £98
  (d) £36   **(e)** £185   **(f)** £135

Make h the subject of each formula.

$$p \quad = h + b \qquad\qquad d \quad = h - b$$

$$\boxed{-b} \quad \boxed{-b} \qquad\qquad \boxed{+b} \quad \boxed{+b}$$

$$p - b = h \qquad\qquad\qquad d + b = h$$
$$h \quad = p - b \qquad\qquad\quad h \quad = d + b$$

4 Make h the subject of each formula.
  (a) $c = h + 7$ **(b)** $f = h + 9$ **(c)** $r = h + 13$
  (d) $p = h + d$ **(e)** $f = h + r$ **(f)** $u = h + i$
  (g) $k = h - 4$ **(h)** $u = h - 8$ **(i)** $s = h - 10$
  (j) $b = h - t$ **(k)** $e = h - u$ **(l)** $w = h - t$
  (m) $j = 4 + h$ **(n)** $w = p + h$ **(o)** $d = e + h$

5 Blair uses $H = 6T$ to find the hire charge for a karaoke machine where H is the hire charge in £ and T is the time in hours.
  (a) Find the hire charge for the following times:
      • 2 hours • 9 hours • 10 hours • 24 hours.
  (b) Find the time when the hire charge is:
      • £24 • £42 • £72 • £54 • £120

The subject of the formula $H = 6T$ is H.
The formula can be rearranged to make T the subject.

$$H \quad = \quad 6T$$

$$\boxed{\div 6} \qquad \boxed{\div 6}$$

$$\frac{H}{6} \quad = \quad T$$

$$T \quad = \quad \frac{H}{6}$$

6 Make T the subject of each formula.
  (a) $H = 7T$ **(b)** $H = 3T$
  (c) $H = 9T$ **(d)** $H = 15T$

7 Blair uses $W = 15T$ to calculate the wages for Tony, his assistant, where W is his wage in £ and T is the number of hours worked.
  (a) How much would Tony be paid for working 20 hours?
  (b) Make T the subject of the formula.
  (c) Use your formula to find the number of hours Tony works to earn £240.

8 Blair calculates the hire cost of different machines using the formula $h = rt$
where h is the hire charge in £
  r is the rate in £ per hour and
  t is the time in hours.

(a) Find the hire charge when a machine is used for 6 hours at a rate of £17 per hour.

(b) The hire charge is £60 for using a machine for 4 hours. What is the rate per hour?

(c) Blair charges £144 for hiring a machine at £16 per hour. For how long has the machine been hired?

The subject of the formula $h = rt$ is h.
The formula can be rearranged to make

- r the subject
  $$h = rt$$
  $\div t$ $\div t$
  $$\frac{h}{t} = r$$
  $$r = \frac{h}{t}$$

- t the subject
  $$h = rt$$
  $\div r$ $\div r$
  $$\frac{h}{r} = t$$
  $$t = \frac{h}{r}$$

9 Make the letter in brackets the subject of each formula.

(a) $d = st$ (s) **(b)** $d = st$ (t)
(c) $v = ir$ (i) **(d)** $v = ir$ (r)
(e) $C = \pi d$ (d) **(f)** $p = 10gh$ (g)

The area of this triangular sign is 1200 cm². Tony's van window is 45 cm high. To find out if the sign will fit in the window: $A = \frac{1}{2}bh$

$\times 2$ $\times 2$
$$2A = bh$$
$\div b$ $\div b$
$$\frac{2A}{b} = h$$
$$h = \frac{2A}{b}$$

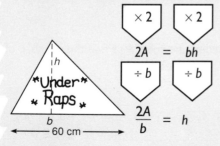

$A = 1200$ cm²

$b = 60$ cm

$$h = \frac{2A}{b}$$

$$h = \frac{2 \times 1200}{60} = 40 \text{ cm}$$

The sign will fit in the van window.

10 (a) Make b the subject of $A = \frac{1}{2}bh$.
(b) Find b when $A = 750$ cm² and $h = 30$ cm.

11 Blair keeps his CDs in a wooden box of volume 16 800 cm³. The volume of the box is given by the formula $V = lbh$
where V is the volume
  l is the length
  b is the breadth and
  h is the height.

(a) Make b the subject of the formula.

(b) Use your formula to find the breadth of the box.

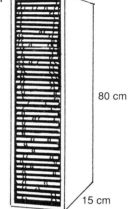

80 cm

15 cm

Tony uses this square advertising sign. Its area is 2500 cm². What is the length of its side?

For a square $A = l^2$
  $\sqrt{A} = l$
  $l = \sqrt{A}$
  $l = \sqrt{2500}$
  $l = 50$

The length of the side is **50 cm**.

12 Use $l = \sqrt{A}$ to find the length of side of squares with area:

(a) 900 cm² **(b)** 625 cm² **(c)** 4225 cm²

13 The area of a circle is given by $A = \pi r^2$ where A is the area and r is the radius of the circle.

(a) Make r the subject of the formula.

(b) Use your formula to find r when:
  • $A = 314$ m² • $A = 28{\cdot}26$ cm²

14 Blair stores his microphones in cylinders. The volume of a cylinder is given by $V = \pi r^2 h$ where V is the volume, r is the radius and h the height.

(a) Make r the subject of the formula.

(b) Find r when $V = 785$ cm³ and $h = 10$ cm.

This roll of carpet fits a square floor. Farah, a carpet fitter, wants to find its length, l.

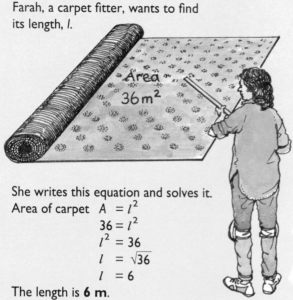

Area 36 m²

She writes this equation and solves it.

Area of carpet $A = l^2$
$$36 = l^2$$
$$l^2 = 36$$
$$l = \sqrt{36}$$
$$l = 6$$

The length is **6 m**.

1 Form an equation and solve it to find the length of side of each carpet square.

(a)

Area 16 m²

(b)

Area 81 m²

(c)

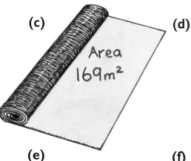

Area 169 m²

(d)

Area 49 m²

(e)

Area 4 m²

(f)

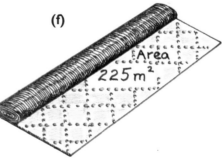

Area 225 m²

2 Find:

(a) $(^-5)^2$ **(b)** $(^-8)^2$ **(c)** $(^-3)^2$

(d) $(^-10)^2$ **(e)** $(^-4)^2$ **(f)** $(^-9)^2$

Farah has noticed that
   if $x = 6$, $x^2 = 36$

   if $x = {}^-6$, $x^2 = 36$

So the solution to the equation $x^2 = 36$ is $x = \pm 6$

$$x^2 = 36$$
$$x = \pm\sqrt{36}$$
$$x = \pm 6$$

3 Solve:

(a) $x^2 = 9$ **(b)** $p^2 = 121$

(c) $a^2 = 4$ **(d)** $w^2 = 1$

4 Solve, expressing answers to 3 significant figures:

(a) $x^2 = 14$ **(b)** $c^2 = 30$ **(c)** $t^2 = 6$

(d) $g^2 = 55$ **(e)** $v^2 = 23{\cdot}8$ **(f)** $s^2 = 0{\cdot}75$

Farah wants to find the length, l, of this room. She writes an equation and solves it.

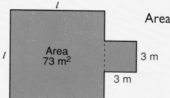

Area 73 m²
l 3 m   3 m

Area of room $= l^2 + 9$
$$l^2 + 9 = 73$$
$$l^2 = 64$$
$$l = \pm\sqrt{64}$$
$$l = \pm 8$$

A length of $^-8$ m is not possible. The length is **8 m**.

5 Form an equation and solve it to find the length, l, of each room.

(a)

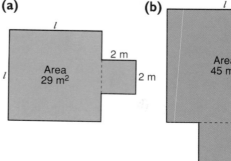

Area 29 m²
l 2 m   2 m

(b)

Area 45 m²
l 3 m   3 m

To find the length, l, of this room.

$l^2 - 9 = 40$
$l^2 = 49$
$l = \pm \sqrt{49}$
$l = \pm 7$

Area
40 m²

3 m

3 m

l

l

A length of ‾7 m is not possible.
The length is **7 m**.

6 Form an equation and solve it to find the length, l, of each room.

(a)

Area
12 m²

2 m
2 m

l

l

(b)

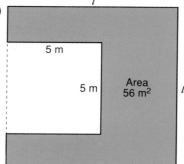

5 m

5 m

Area
56 m²

l

l

Farah can solve equations like these.

$x^2 + 7 = 43$
$x^2 \quad = 36$
$x \quad = \pm \sqrt{36}$
$x \quad = \pm 6$

$y^2 - 9 = 91$
$y^2 \quad = 100$
$y \quad = \pm \sqrt{100}$
$y \quad = \pm 10$

7 Solve:

(a) $x^2 + 6 = 70$ (b) $f^2 + 3 = 84$
(c) $r^2 + 9 = 25$ (d) $v^2 - 6 = 10$
(e) $b^2 - 4 = 96$ (f) $b^2 - 17 = 127$
(g) $d^2 + 12 = 76$ (h) $p^2 + 19 = 55$

Farah wants to find the breadth, b, of this room.

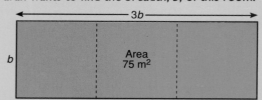

3b

b

Area
75 m²

She writes an equation and solves it.
Area $= 3b \times b = 3b^2$
$3b^2 \quad = 75$
$b^2 \quad = 25$
$b \quad = \pm \sqrt{25}$
$b \quad = \pm 5$

A breadth of ‾5 m is not possible.
The breadth is **5 m.**

8 Form an equation and solve it to find the breadth, b, of each room.

(a) b

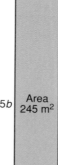

5b

Area
245 m²

(b) b

3b

Area
243 m²

(c) b

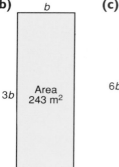
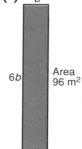

6b

Area
96 m²

Farah can solve equations like this.

$6x^2 = 216$
$x^2 = 36$
$x = \pm \sqrt{36}$
$x = \pm 6$

9 Solve:

(a) $2x^2 = 50$ (b) $3s^2 = 48$
(c) $5c^2 = 20$ (d) $4y^2 = 36$
(e) $9p^2 = 9$ (f) $6v^2 = 150$
(g) $8f^2 = 72$ (h) $6s^2 = 384$

Farah can solve equations like these:

$$6x^2 + 5 = 155 \qquad 8p^2 - 9 = 47$$
$$6x^2 = 150 \qquad 8p^2 = 56$$
$$x^2 = 25 \qquad p^2 = 7$$
$$x = \pm \sqrt{25} \qquad p = \pm \sqrt{7}$$
$$x = \pm 5 \qquad p = \pm 2 \cdot 65$$
$$\text{(to 3 sig figs)}$$

1 Solve:
(a) $3x^2 + 7 = 82$ (b) $2v^2 + 5 = 37$
(c) $7c^2 + 12 = 19$ (d) $8p^2 - 7 = 193$
(e) $4d^2 - 9 = 135$ (f) $7c^2 - 6 = 57$

2 Solve, expressing answers to 3 significant figures:
(a) $b^2 - 7 = 35$ (b) $h^2 + 9 = 67$
(c) $v^2 - 6 = 78$ (d) $5c^2 = 40$
(e) $7f^2 = 84$ (f) $6t^2 - 5 = 43$
(g) $4b^2 + 9 = 61$ (h) $8t^2 - 15 = 58$

Equations can be solved by trial and improvement. To find the length, l, of this room, Farah writes an equation and solves it.

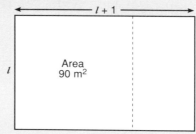

Area $= l(l + 1) = l^2 + l$ and   Area $= 90 \text{ m}^2$
$l^2 + l = 90$
Try 8 $8^2 + 8 = 64 + 8 = 72$ Too low
Try 10 $10^2 + 10 = 100 + 10 = 110$ Too high

The answer lies between 8 and 10

Try 9 $9^2 + 9 = 90$

The solution to $l^2 + l = 90$ is $l = 9$

3 Solve:
(a) $x^2 + x = 20$ (b) $x^2 + x = 72$
(c) $x^2 + x = 12$ (d) $x^2 - x = 90$
(e) $x^2 - x = 30$ (f) $x^2 - x = 42$

Not all equations have whole number solutions. Solve $x^2 + x = 5$, giving the answer correct to 2 significant figures.

Try 1 $1^2 + 1 = 2$ Too low
Try 2 $2^2 + 2 = 6$ Too high

x lies between 1 and 2

Try 1·6 $1 \cdot 6^2 + 1 \cdot 6 = 4 \cdot 16$ Too low
Try 1·9 $1 \cdot 9^2 + 1 \cdot 9 = 5 \cdot 51$ Too high

x lies between 1·6 and 1·9

Try 1·7 $1 \cdot 7^2 + 1 \cdot 7 = 4 \cdot 59$ Too low
Try 1·8 $1 \cdot 8^2 + 1 \cdot 8 = 5 \cdot 04$ Too high

x lies between 1·7 and 1·8

Try 1·75 $1 \cdot 75^2 + 1 \cdot 75 = 4 \cdot 8125$ Too low

The solution to $x^2 + x = 5$ is **$x = 1 \cdot 8$** to 2 sig figs.

4 Solve, giving answers correct to 2 significant figures:
(a) $x^2 + x = 9$ (b) $x^2 + x = 13$
(c) $x^2 + x = 28$ (d) $x^2 - x = 18$
(e) $x^2 - x = 50$ (f) $x^2 - x = 75$
(g) $x^2 + x = 130$ (h) $x^2 - x = 33$

◤ **Challenge**

5 **Without** using the $\sqrt{}$ button on your calculator, find the length of the side of this square, correct to 3 significant figures.

You need a pair of compasses, a ruler, card and sheets of A4 paper.

1 (a) On card construct an equilateral triangle of side 3 cm.
   (b) Cut out the triangle and mark one corner with a dot.
   (c) In the centre of an A4 sheet of paper draw a 9 cm square.
   (d) Starting at one corner of the square 'roll' the card triangle along each **outside edge**. Draw the locus of the **corner with the dot**.
   (e) Now roll the card triangle **inside** the 9 cm square and draw the locus.

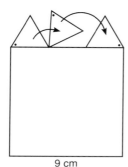

9 cm

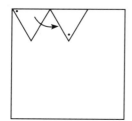

2 Draw a rectangle 9 cm by 12 cm in the centre of an A4 sheet of paper. Repeat question 1 for this rectangle.

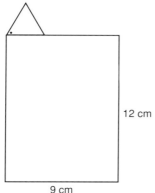

12 cm

9 cm

3 (a) On a 3 cm square piece of card mark one corner with a dot.
   (b) Draw a 9 cm square in the centre of an A4 sheet of paper.
   (c) Starting at one corner of the square roll the card square round each outside edge. Draw the locus of the corner with the dot.
   (d) Now roll the card square inside the 9 cm square and draw the locus.

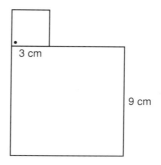

3 cm

9 cm

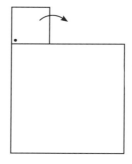

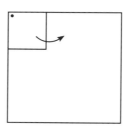

4 Draw a rectangle 9 cm by 12 cm in the centre of an A4 sheet of paper. Repeat question 3 for this rectangle.

1 The chemical formula for water is H_2O. This means that 2 hydrogen atoms are joined to each oxygen atom.

(a) What is the ratio of hydrogen atoms to oxygen atoms?

(b) How many hydrogen atoms are joined to 1000 oxygen atoms?

(c) How many oxygen atoms are required for 5000 hydrogen atoms?

(d) If there are 3600 atoms altogether, how many will be:
  • hydrogen   • oxygen?

2 Copper oxide contains copper and oxygen atoms. In an experiment, 36 g of the oxide produced 32 g of copper.

Write, in simplest form, the fraction of the total mass which is:

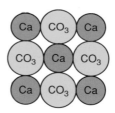

(a) copper   (b) oxygen.

3 At high temperatures calcium carbonate breaks down into calcium oxide and carbon dioxide, in the ratio 14 : 11. What mass of each would be produced from 100 g of calcium carbonate?

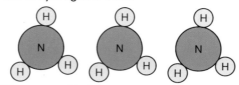

4 In ammonia the ratio of the mass of nitrogen to the mass of hydrogen is 14 : 3.

What mass of hydrogen is required for 120 g of nitrogen? Write your answer to 2 decimal places.

5 When iron ore is heated in a furnace, $\frac{7}{10}$ of its mass is turned into iron.

(a) How many kilograms of iron are produced from 1 tonne of ore?

(b) How much ore, to nearest kg, is required to produce 1000 kg of iron?

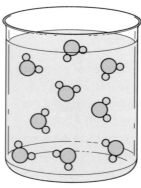

6 Calcium carbonate consists of 40% calcium, 12% carbon and 48% oxygen. What fraction is:

(a) calcium   (b) carbon   (c) oxygen?

7 It takes 80 g of copper oxide to make 135 g of copper chloride.

What mass of copper oxide is needed to make 2·7 g of copper chloride?

8 A sample of carbon monoxide contains 12 g of carbon and 16 g of oxygen.

(a) What fraction of the total mass is:
  • carbon   • oxygen?

(b) What percentage of the total mass is:
  • carbon   • oxygen?

(c) What mass of carbon is there in 33 g of carbon monoxide? Write your answer to 2 decimal places.

9 A sample of carbon dioxide contains 12 g of carbon and 32 g of oxygen.

(a) What fraction of the total mass is:
  • carbon   • oxygen?

(b) What percentage of the total mass is:
  • carbon   • oxygen?

(c) What mass of carbon is there in 56 g of carbon dioxide? Write your answer to 3 significant figures.

These **hydrocarbons** are extracted from oil. They contain hydrogen and carbon atoms.

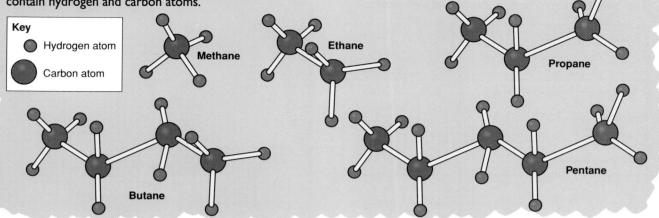

Where necessary, answers should be rounded to 1 decimal place.

10 For each hydrocarbon write, in simplest form, the ratio of carbon atoms to hydrogen atoms.

11 The chemical formulae for some hydrocarbons are given below.

Methane CH_4 Ethane C_2H_6 Propane C_3H_8

(a) What is the chemical formula for Butane?
(b) Hexane has 6 carbon atoms. Copy and complete the formula for Hexane.
$C_6H_\square$
(c) Write the chemical formula for Octane.

12 The atomic mass of each carbon atom is 12 units, and of each hydrogen atom, 1 unit.

(a) Copy and complete the table for these hydrocarbons.

Hydrocarbon	Mass of carbon	Mass of hydrogen	Molecular mass
Methane	12 units	4 units	16 units
Ethane	24 units	6 units	30 units
Propane			

(b) Write the ratio of the mass of carbon to the mass of hydrogen in a molecule of:
• Methane   • Propane   • Pentane.
(c) What percentage of the molecular mass is hydrogen in each of these molecules?
• Ethane   • Butane   • Pentane

13

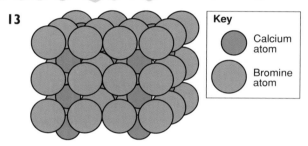

In the diagram, 2 atoms of bromine are linked to 1 of calcium to produce calcium bromide. The atomic mass of bromine is 80 units, and of calcium is 40 units.

(a) What fraction of the total mass is:
• calcium   • bromine?
(b) What percentage of the total mass is:
• calcium   • bromine?

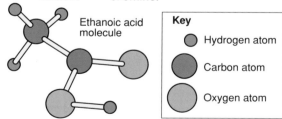

14 Ethanoic acid is mixed with water to make vinegar. In the molecule shown, there are 2 atoms of carbon, 4 atoms of hydrogen and 2 atoms of oxygen. The atomic mass of carbon is 12 units, of hydrogen is 1 unit and of oxygen is 16 units. In each ethanoic acid molecule,

(a) what fraction of the total mass is:
• carbon   • hydrogen   • oxygen
(b) what percentage of the total mass is:
• carbon   • hydrogen   • oxygen?

Scientists use many different formulae and data.
This table lists scientific data about several elements.

Element	Mass in g	Volume in cm^3	Melting point in°C	Boiling point in °C
Aluminium	20·25	7·5	660	2470
Bromine	12·48	4	⁻7	59
Carbon (diamond)	8·78	2·5	3750	——
Krypton	75·6	35	⁻157	⁻152
Lead	11·3	1	327	1744
Mercury	92·5	6·8	⁻39	357
Plutonium	9·9	0·5	640	3240
Radon	1·1	0·25	⁻71	⁻62

1 (a) List the elements in order of their melting points. Start with the highest value.
  (b) List the elements in order of their boiling points. Start with the lowest value.

2 Find the difference between the melting point and the boiling point of:
  (a) aluminium   (b) bromine
  (c) mercury   (d) krypton
  (e) radon.

3 The density of a quantity is calculated using this formula: $\rho = \dfrac{m}{v}$
  where ρ is the density in grams per cm^3
  m is the mass in grams and
  v is the volume in cm^3
  (a) Use the information in the table.
  Calculate, to 1 decimal place, the density of:
  • aluminium   • carbon (diamond)
  • krypton   • lead.
  (b) List these elements in order of density, starting with the greatest.

4 Temperature can be measured in degrees Kelvin. The formula for converting from degrees Celsius to degrees Kelvin is: $K = C + 273$
  where K is the number of degrees Kelvin and
  C is the number of degrees Celsius.
  (a) Find the melting point, in degrees Kelvin, of:
  • bromine   • lead
  • mercury   • plutonium.
  (b) **Absolute zero** is 0° Kelvin. Write this in degrees Celsius.

5 The boiling point, in degrees Fahrenheit, of some elements is given in the table.

Elements	Boiling point °F
Iron	5432
Platinum	8186
Xenon	⁻162
Neon	⁻411

The formula for converting from degrees Fahrenheit to degrees Kelvin is:

$$K = \frac{5(F - 32)}{9} + 273$$

where K is the number of degrees Kelvin and
F is the number of degrees Fahrenheit.
  (a) Find the boiling point, in degrees Kelvin, of each element.
  (b) Express Absolute zero in degrees Fahrenheit.

Where necessary, round answers to 1 decimal place.

6 The velocity of a particle can be calculated using the
formula: $v = u + at$

where v is the velocity in ms^{-1}

$\quad$ u is the initial velocity in ms^{-1}

$\quad$ a is the acceleration in ms^{-2} and

$\quad$ t is the time in seconds.

(a) Calculate the velocity of each particle.

Particle	u	a	t
α	5	10	3
β	$^-$4	12	8
χ	8	$^-$10	9
γ	$^-$6	$^-$4	5

(b) The acceleration of particles can be found using
the formula:

$$a = \frac{(v - u)}{t}$$

Calculate the acceleration when:
- $v = 12.6$, $u = 5.2$ and $t = 3.5$
- $v = 250$, $u = 0$ and $t = 60$

7 When a substance is heated, the heat energy gained
is calculated using the formula:

$\quad E = mc(t_2 - t_1)$

where E is the heat energy gained in Joules

$\quad$ m is the mass in kg

$\quad$ c is the specific heat capacity in Joules/kg $°$C

$\quad t_1$ is the initial temperature in $°$C and

$\quad t_2$ is the final temperature in $°$C.

Calculate E when:

(a) $m = 1.5$, $c = 386$, $t_1 = 35$ and $t_2 = 45$

(b) $m = 0.6$, $c = 2350$, $t_1 = 78$ and $t_2 = 82$

(c) 2 kg of water, with specific heat capacity
4180 J/kg$°$C, is heated from 25$°$C to 30$°$C.

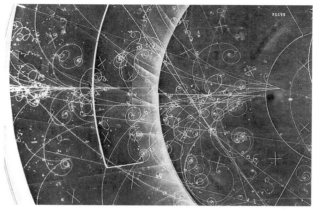

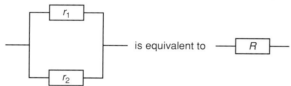

is equivalent to

8 In an electrical circuit with two resistors, r_1 and r_2 in
parallel, the equivalent resistance, R ohms, is given by
the formula:

$$R = \frac{r_1 r_2}{(r_1 + r_2)}$$

Calculate R when:

(a) $r_1 = 1.5$ and $r_2 = 1.6$

(b) $r_1 = 12.3$ and $r_2 = 0.6$

9 The focal length of a lens in a telescope can be
calculated using the formula:

$$f = \frac{vu}{(v + u)}$$

where f is the focal length,

$\quad$ v is the image distance from the pole of the
lens, and

$\quad$ u is the object distance from the pole of the
lens.

Calculate f when:

(a) $v = 1.2$ and $u = 1500$

(b) $v = 0.56$ and $u = 6100$

Much ado about Nothings

Scientists often work with very large numbers. For example, the amount of energy given out by the Sun every second is about 100 000 000 000 000 000 000 Joules.
Numbers like this can be written in a shorter form.

$100 = 10 \times 10 = 10^2$ We can read this as 10 to the power 2.

$1000 = 10 \times 10 \times 10 = 10^3$ We can read this as 10 to the power 3.

So the amount of energy given out by the Sun every second is about **10^{20} Joules**.

1 Rewrite each sentence expressing the number as a power of 10.
   (a) The height of Mount Everest is about 10 000 metres.
   (b) Man has inhabited the Earth for about 100 000 years.

2 Write each number as a power of 10.
   (a) 1 000 000   **(b)** 1000 000 000
   (c) 10 000 000   **(d)** 1 000 000 000 000 000 000

3 Rewrite these sentences expressing each number in full.
   (a) The mass of 1 cubic metre of water is 10^3 kg.
   (b) The amount of energy discharged in a flash of lightning is 10^9 Joules.
   (c) The radius of the galaxy is about 10^{19} metres.

4 Write each number in full.
   (a) 10^6 **(b)** 10^{12} **(c)** 10^8 **(d)** 10^{11}

A rocket has to travel at a speed of 40 000 km/h to escape the effect of the Earth's gravity.

40 000 can be written as $4 \times 10 000$
$= 4 \times 10^4$

This method of writing numbers is called **standard form** or **scientific notation**.

5 Rewrite each sentence expressing the number in standard form.
   (a) The human ear cannot hear above about 20 000 Hertz.
   (b) The radius of the Earth is about 5 000 000 metres.
   (c) The mass of the Earth is about 6 000 000 000 000 000 000 000 000 kg.

6 Write in scientific notation:
   (a) 3 000 000   **(b)** 50 000
   (c) 900 000 000   **(d)** 20 000 000 000
   (e) 7 000 000 000   **(f)** 8 000 000 000 000 000

7 Rewrite each sentence expressing the number in full.
   (a) The speed of light is about 3×10^8 m/s.
   (b) The age of the Earth is about 6×10^9 years.
   (c) The energy released by an earthquake can be of the order of 4×10^{17} Joules.

8 Write each number in full.
   (a) 2×10^5 **(b)** 5×10^8
   (c) 9×10^{13} **(d)** 7×10^{15}

The table shows data for the Solar System.

Planet	Average distance from the Sun (km)	Circumference (km)	Escape velocity (km/h)	Number of moons
Mercury	58 000 000	15 300	15 000	0
Venus	108 000 000	38 000	37 200	0
Earth	150 000 000	40 070	40 000	1
Mars	228 000 000	21 340	18 100	2
Jupiter	778 000 000	449 000	216 800	16
Saturn	1 427 000 000	380 000	116 000	23
Uranus	2 870 000 000	165 900	81 000	15
Neptune	4 497 000 000	152 000	86 040	8
Pluto	5 899 000 000	9000	unknown	1
Sun	0	4 370 000	2 220 000	0

The average distance of Mercury from the Sun is 58 000 000 km.

This can be written in **standard form** or **scientific notation**.

$$58\,000\,000 = 5{\cdot}8 \times 10\,000\,000 = 5{\cdot}8 \times 10^7$$

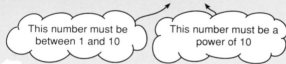

This number must be between 1 and 10

This number must be a power of 10

1 Write in standard form:

(a) the circumference of Earth
(b) the escape velocity of Jupiter
(c) the average distance of Mars from the Sun
(d) the average distance of Venus from the Sun
(e) the circumference of the Sun
(f) the number of moons of Saturn.

2 Which planet has:

(a) an escape velocity of $8{\cdot}1 \times 10^4$ km/h
(b) a distance from the Sun of $7{\cdot}78 \times 10^8$ km
(c) a circumference of 9×10^3 km
(d) $1{\cdot}6 \times 10$ moons?

3 (a) Write in scientific notation:
• the circumference of Neptune
• the circumference of Mercury.
(b) Which has the greater circumference?

4 (a) Write in standard form:
• the average distance of Neptune from the Sun
• the average distance of Pluto from the Sun.
(b) How much further from the Sun is Pluto than Neptune?

The mathematical notation for standard form or scientific notation is

$$a \times 10^n$$

where $1 \leqslant a < 10$ and n is an integer.

a is a number between 1 and 10

The circumference of Mars is $2{\cdot}134 \times 10^4$.
In this example, $a = 2{\cdot}143$ and $n = 4$

5 (a) Write in the form $a \times 10^n$ where a is a number between 1 and 10 and n is an integer:
• the escape velocity from the Sun
• the escape velocity from Earth.
(b) Why do you think it requires a greater escape velocity from the Sun than from Earth?

6 The numbers in these statements are written in the form $a \times 10^n$ where $1 \leqslant a < 10$ and n is an integer. For each write • the value of a • the value of n.

(a) The circumference of Venus is $3{\cdot}8 \times 10^4$ km.
(b) The escape velocity from Saturn is $1{\cdot}16 \times 10^5$ km/h.

Scientists also work with very small numbers.

The diameter of a hydrogen atom is about 0·000 000 000 001 m.

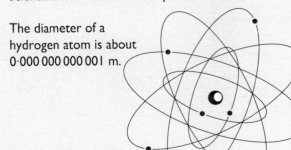

Numbers like this can be written in a shorter form.

$$10\,000 = 10^4$$
$$1000 = 10^3$$
$$100 = 10^2$$
$$10 = 10^1$$
$$1 = 10^0$$
$$0·1 = 10^{-1}$$
$$0·01 = 10^{-2}$$
$$0·001 = 10^{-3}$$
$$0·000\,1 = 10^{-4}$$

So the diameter of a hydrogen atom is about 10^{-12} m.

1 Rewrite each sentence expressing the number as a power of 10.

  (a) The thickness of this page is about 0·000 1 m.

  (b) A camera shutter speed can be 0·01 second.

  (c) The radius of a nucleus is about 0·000 000 000 000 01 m.

2 Write each number as a power of 10.

  (a) 0·000 000 000 1   **(b)** 0·000 000 1

  (c) 0·000 000 000 000 001

  (d) 0·000 000 000 000 000 000 01

3 Rewrite these sentences expressing each number in full.

  (a) Microwave radiation can have a wavelength of 10^{-3} m.

  (b) A nanometre is 10^{-9} of a metre.

  (c) The wavelength of visible light is between about 10^{-7} m and 10^{-6} m.

4 Write each number in full.

  (a) 10^{-5} **(b)** 10^{-1} **(c)** 10^{-9} **(d)** 10^{-12}

Light travels 1 metre in about 0·000 000 003 seconds.

This can be written in standard form or scientific notation.

$$0·000\,000\,003 = 3 \times 0·000\,000\,001$$
$$= 3 \times 10^{-9}$$

The half-life of plutonium is 0·000 15 seconds.

This can be written in standard form or scientific notation.

$$0·000\,15 = 1·5 \times 0·000\,1$$
$$= 1·5 \times 10^{-4}$$

5 Rewrite each sentence expressing the number in scientific notation.

  (a) Some X-rays have a wavelength of 0·000 000 000 5 m.

  (b) One second is equivalent to 0·000 000 031 69 of a year.

  (c) The Bohr radius of an atom is 0·000 000 000 052 9 m.

6 Write in standard form:

  (a) 0·000 4   **(b)** 0·000 005 6   **(c)** 0·032 4

  (d) 0·000 000 000 788   **(e)** 0·000 010 3

  (f) 0·000 000 900 8   **(g)** 0·246

  (h) 2 890 000   **(i)** 456 000 000 000

  (j) 906 000   **(k)** 35 000 000 000 000 000

7 Rewrite each sentence expressing the number in full.

  (a) The mass of a proton is $1·673 \times 10^{-27}$ kg.

  (b) The charge of an electron is $1·602 \times 10^{-19}$ C.

  (c) Avogadro's number is $6·023 \times 10^{23}$

  (d) The speed of light is $2·998 \times 10^8$ m/s.

  (e) The mass of a proton is equal to the mass of $1·84 \times 10^3$ electrons.

The speed of light is 3.0×10^8 m/s.
How far will light travel in 5 seconds?

Distance = Speed × Time
$$= 3.0 \times 10^8 \times 5$$
$$= 300\,000\,000 \times 5$$
$$= 1\,500\,000\,000$$

Light will travel $1\,500\,000\,000$ m or 1.5×10^9 **m** in 5 seconds.

This calculation can be carried out using a scientific calculator.

Enter **3.0** Press **exp** **8** .

To give **3.   08**

Some calculators have an **E** or **EE** button instead of **exp**

Now press **×** **5** **=**

To give **1.5   09**

This means 1.5×10^9

Light will travel 1.5×10^9 **m** in 5 seconds.

Use a scientific calculator. Express answers in scientific notation.

1 How far will light travel in:
(a) 8 seconds   (b) 1·5 seconds
(c) 6·8 seconds   (d) 70 seconds?

2 There are 6.02×10^{23} particles in 1 mole of carbon. How many particles are there in:
(a) 8 moles   (b) 2·5 moles   (c) 50 moles?

3 Calculate:
(a) $2.3 \times 10^4 \times 6$ (b) $4.6 \times 10^9 \times 3.6$
(c) $5.7 \times 10^2 \times 3.31$ (d) $5.23 \times 10^{27} \times 8.9$
(e) $2.998 \times 10^8 \times 6.7$ (f) $4000 \times 3.56 \times 10^9$

How far will light travel in 5×10^4 seconds?
Distance = Speed × Time
$$= 3.0 \times 10^8 \times 5 \times 10^4$$

Enter **3.0**

Press **exp** **8** **×** **5** **exp** **4** **=**

To give **1.5   13**

This means 1.5×10^{13}

Light will travel 1.5×10^{13} m in 5×10^4 seconds.

4 How far will light travel in:
(a) 8.3×10^{12} seconds   (b) 3.5×10^{16} seconds
(c) 7.3×10^{27} seconds   (d) 6.675×10^{35} seconds?

5 Calculate:
(a) $2.3 \times 10^4 \times 6 \times 10^8$ (b) $4.6 \times 10^9 \times 3.6 \times 10^3$
(c) $9.7 \times 10^4 \times 3.69 \times 10^5$
(d) $7.23 \times 10^{27} \times 1.9 \times 10^{18}$
(e) $2.38 \times 10^2 \times 6.3 \times 10^8$ (f) $3.56 \times 10^9 \times 4 \times 10^8$

The Sun is 1.5×10^{11} m from Earth.
How long does it take sunlight to reach Earth?
Time = Distance ÷ Speed
$$= (1.5 \times 10^{11}) \div (3 \times 10^8)$$

Enter **1.5**

Press **exp** **11** **÷** **3** **exp** **8** **=**

To give **5   02**

It takes 5×10^2 **seconds (or 500 seconds)** for sunlight to reach Earth.

6 How long does light take to reach each of these planets?

Planet	Average distance from the Sun (m)
Mercury	5.8×10^{10}
Mars	2.28×10^{11}
Jupiter	7.78×10^{11}
Pluto	5.899×10^{12}

You need a pair of compasses.

Joe is marking out a new rose bed in the park.

Joe ties the ends of a 10 metre rope to two pegs, A and B, which are 8 metres apart. He moves round, keeping the rope taut, and marking the ground at regular intervals.

1 (a) Copy and complete the table.

Distance from peg A in metres	5	6	4	7	3	8	2	9	1
Distance from peg B in metres	5	4	6						

(b) Make a scale drawing of Joe's rose bed using a scale of 1 cm to 1 m.
- Mark points A and B.
- Use the distances from the table and compasses to find the position of each mark.
- Join the points in a smooth curve to show the outline of the rose bed.

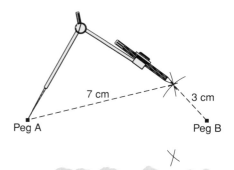

7 cm   3 cm

Peg A   Peg B

The shape you have drawn is called an **ellipse**.

2 Joe tries a different position for the pegs. He places them 6 metres apart.

(a) Copy and complete the table.

Distance from peg A in metres	5	6	4	7	3	8	2
Distance from peg B in metres	5	4	6				

(b) Make a scale drawing of the rose bed.

3 Make a table of distances and then a scale drawing of each ellipse.

Ellipse	Distance between pegs	Length of rope
a	4 m	10 m
b	8 m	12 m
c	9 m	14 m

4 If Joe ties both ends of the rope to a single peg what shape would he make?

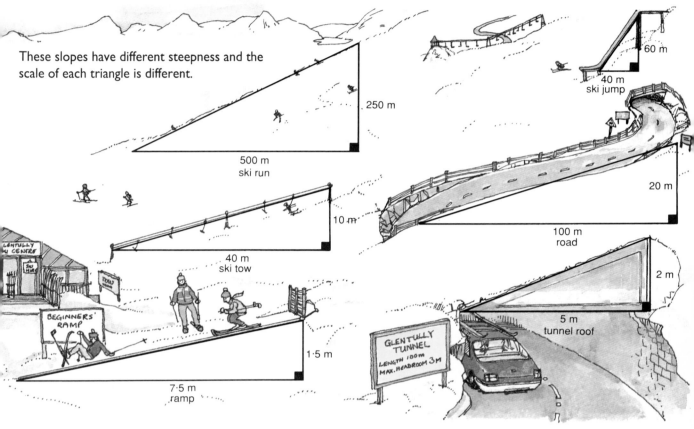

These slopes have different steepness and the scale of each triangle is different.

250 m

500 m
ski run

60 m
40 m
ski jump

20 m

100 m
road

10 m

40 m
ski tow

2 m

5 m
tunnel roof

1·5 m

7·5 m
ramp

GLENTULLY
TUNNEL
LENGTH 100m
MAX. HEADROOM 3M

Work with a partner.

1 Discuss the slopes above and list them in order of steepness.

Gradient is a measure of steepness.
Gradient is calculated using this formula:
Gradient = distance up ÷ distance along

For the ski tow

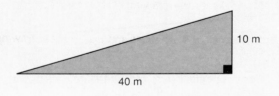

10 m

40 m

distance up   = 10 m
distance along   = 40 m

Gradient = distance up ÷ distance along
         = 10 ÷ 40
         = **0·25**

2 (a) Calculate the gradient of the other slopes.
   (b) Compare these gradients with your list from question 1.

3 Calculate the gradient of each slope.

(a)

3 m

5 m

(b)

100 m

400 m

(c)

4 m

3 m

(d)

1·5 m

4·5 m

(e)

2·7 m

13·5 m

TO THE
BEACH

(f)

5 m

2 m

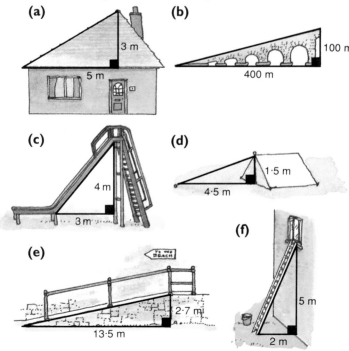

Life's Ups and Downs

To find the gradients of the lines AB and CD:

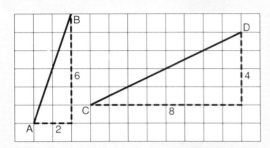

Gradient of AB = distance up ÷ distance along
= 6 ÷ 2
= **3**

Gradient of CD = distance up ÷ distance along
= 4 ÷ 8
= **0·5**

1 Calculate the gradient of each line.

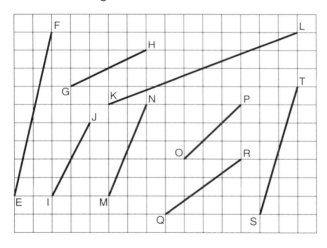

2 Plot the points P(0,1) and Q(2,5). Join them with a straight line, and find its gradient.

3 Find the gradient of the straight line joining each pair of points.

(a) (1,2) and (3,6)　　(b) (2,0) and (5,9)
(c) (2,3) and (4,6)　　(d) (0,3) and (1,8)
(e) (⁻1,2) and (3,8)　　(f) (⁻2,⁻3) and (0,4)
(g) (⁻3,⁻4) and (⁻1,⁻1)　　(h) (⁻1,5) and (5,10)
(i) (2,5) and (0,1)　　(j) (6,8) and (2,2)

All the gradients calculated so far have been **positive**. The lines have sloped up from left to right across the page.
Lines that slope downwards from left to right across the page have a **negative** gradient.

To find the gradients of the lines KL and MN:

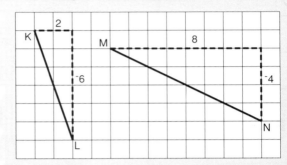

Gradient of KL = distance up ÷ distance along
= ⁻6 ÷ 2
= **⁻3**

Gradient of MN = distance up ÷ distance along
= ⁻4 ÷ 8
= **⁻0·5**

4 Calculate the gradient of each line.

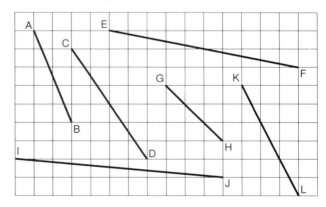

5 Plot the points P(1,7) and Q(4,1). Join them with a straight line and find its gradient.

6 Find the gradient of the straight line joining each pair of points.

(a) (1,7) and (3,1)　　(b) (2,6) and (3,2)
(c) (2,10) and (4,6)　　(d) (0,3) and (3,0)
(e) (1,2) and (3,⁻8)　　(f) (⁻2,3) and (0,⁻4)
(g) (3,⁻4) and (1,⁻1)　　(h) (⁻1,5) and (5,0)

7 Calculate the gradient of each line.

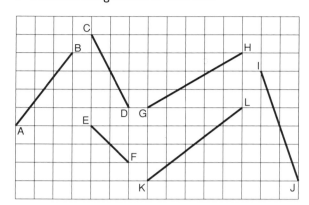

8 ▶ Do Worksheet 14, question 1.

Any two points on a straight line can be used to find its gradient.

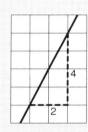

Gradient = distance up ÷ distance along
= 4 ÷ 2
= **2**
The gradient of the line is 2.

9 Find the gradient of each line.

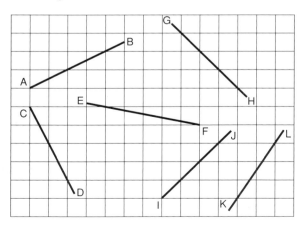

10 ▶ Do Worksheet 14, question 2.

Lines with the same gradient are parallel.

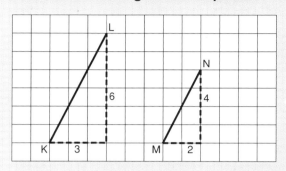

Gradient of KL = distance up ÷ distance along
= 6 ÷ 3
= **2**
Gradient of MN = distance up ÷ distance along
= 4 ÷ 2
= **2**
Since the gradients are equal,
KL and MN are parallel.

11 (a) Calculate the gradient of each line.

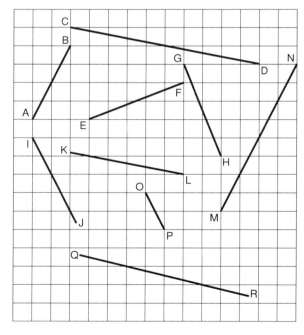

(b) List pairs of parallel lines.

Towing the line

Franz is the engineer with the Glentully Ski Company.
The distance travelled on this chairlift is found
using the formula
$$d = 4t$$
where d is the distance travelled in metres and
t is the time in seconds.
Franz has completed this table and drawn a graph.

t	1	2	3	4
d	4	8	12	16

The speed of the chairlift is **4 m/s**.

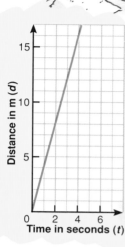

1 The speed of the chairlift is increased to 5 m/s.
   The formula is $d = 5t$.
   Make a table and draw a graph to show this
   information.

2 Draw a graph to show each formula.
   (a) $d = 2t$ **(b)** $d = 3t$ **(c)** $d = \frac{1}{2}t$ **(d)** $d = t$

3 **(a)** Calculate the gradient of each line in your
       answers to question **2**.
   (b) Copy and complete.

Formula	$d = 2t$	$d = 3t$	$d = \frac{1}{2}t$	$d = t$
Gradient				

   (c) What do you notice?

4 For each equation:
   • make a table   • draw a graph
   • calculate the gradient of the line.
   (a) $y = 3x$ **(b)** $y = {}^{-}2x$
   (c) $y = \frac{-1}{2}x$ **(d)** $y = \frac{1}{4}x$

5 What do you notice about your answers to
   question **4**?

When an equation is of the form $y = mx$
• its graph is a straight line
• the gradient of the line is m and
• the line passes through the origin.
The graph of $y = 2x$ is a straight line, has gradient 2
and passes through the origin.

6 Without drawing, write the gradient of the line with
   equation:
   (a) $y = 5x$ **(b)** $y = 8x$ **(c)** $y = 6x$
   (d) $y = \frac{3}{4}x$ **(e)** $y = {}^{-}5x$ **(f)** $y = {}^{-}6x$
   (g) $y = {}^{-}99x$ **(h)** $y = {}^{-}1 \cdot 5x$ **(i)** $y = 14x$

7 Franz is checking the amount of fuel used to run a
   ski tow.

Fuel used in litres (f)	1	2	3	4
Time in hours (t)	5	10	15	20

   (a) Draw a graph to show this information.
   (b) Extend the line and check that it passes through
       the origin.
   (c) Calculate the gradient of the line.
   (d) Copy and complete the formula: $f = \boxed{} t$

8 For each table:
   • draw a graph to show the information
   • extend the line and check that it passes through the
     origin
   • calculate the gradient of the line
   • copy and complete the formula: $f = \boxed{} t$

(a)

Fuel used in litres (f)	1	2	3	4
Time in hours (t)	2	4	6	8

(b)

Fuel used in litres (f)	1	2	3	4
Time in hours (t)	0·5	1	1·5	2

(c)

Fuel used in litres (f)	2	4	6	8
Time in hours (t)	5	10	15	20

1 For each graph:
  • calculate the gradient of the line
  • write the equation of the line.

(a)

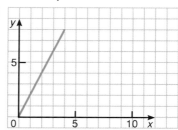

(b)

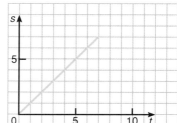

(c)

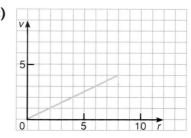

(d)

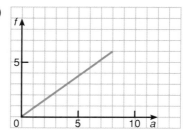

(e)

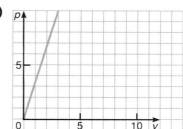

(f)

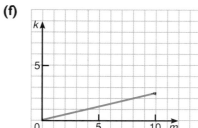

(g)

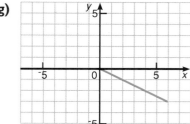

(h)

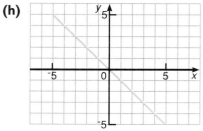

Safe as houses!

The Jackson's house has been struck by a large tree. They have organised emergency repairs.

You need 2 mm squared paper.

1 Theo is a plumber. For emergency repairs he charges £15 per hour plus a call-out fee of £10. He uses this formula to prepare his bill:

$C = 15t + 10$ where C is the cost in £

and t is the time in hours.

(a) Copy and complete the table and graph.

Time in hours (t)	1	2	3	4	5
Cost in £ (C)	25				

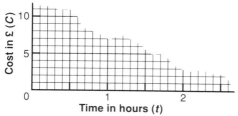

(b) At what point will the line cut the Cost axis?

2 Dawn is a glazier. She uses this formula to calculate her charges for emergency repairs:

$C = 12t + 16$ where C is the cost in £

and t is the time in hours.

(a) Copy and complete the table.

Time in hours (t)	1	2	3	4	5
Cost in £ (C)					

(b) Choose suitable scales and draw a graph.

(c) At what point will the line cut the Cost axis?

3 Sulamith is a locksmith. She uses this formula to calculate her charges for emergency repairs:

$C = 16t + 20$ where C is the cost in £

and t is the time in hours.

(a) Make a table and draw a graph.

(b) At what point will the line cut the Cost axis?

4 Mark is a carpenter. He uses this formula to calculate his charges for emergency repairs:

$C = 20t + 10$ where C is the cost in £

and t is the time in hours.

(a) Make a table and draw a graph.

(b) At what point will the line cut the Cost axis?

5 (a) Copy and complete the table for the graphs you have drawn.

Equation	$C = 15t + 10$	$C = 12t + 16$
Point where line cuts the Cost axis	(0,)	

(b) Write about what you notice.

Tara made a table and drew the graph of the equation $y = 3x + 1$

x	0	1	2	3
y	1	4	7	10
Point	(0,1)	(1,4)	(2,7)	(3,10)

Tara plotted the points and joined them up.
She extended the line and labelled it.

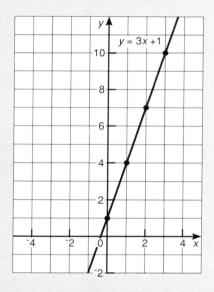

1 **(a)** On the same diagram draw this family of lines:
   Family R $y = x + 2$
   $\qquad\qquad y = 2x + 2$
   $\qquad\qquad y = 3x + 2.$
   (b) What do you notice about the point where the lines cut the y-axis?

2 Repeat question 1 for each of these families of lines.

   Family S $y = x + 3$ $\qquad$ **Family T** $y = x + 4$
   $\qquad\qquad y = 2x + 3$ $\qquad\qquad\qquad\quad y = 2x + 4$
   $\qquad\qquad y = 3x + 3$ $\qquad\qquad\qquad\quad y = 3x + 4$

   Family U $y = x + 5$ $\qquad$ **Family V** $y = x - 1$
   $\qquad\qquad y = 2x + 5$ $\qquad\qquad\qquad\quad y = 2x - 1$
   $\qquad\qquad y = 3x + 5$ $\qquad\qquad\qquad\quad y = 3x - 1$

When the equation of a line is in the form
$\qquad y = mx + c$
• its graph is a straight line
• the line cuts the y-axis at $(0,c)$.

The line $y = 3x + 5$ cuts the y-axis at $(0,5)$

The line $y = 2x - 4$ cuts the y-axis at $(0, {}^-4)$

3 Write the coordinates of the point where the graph of each equation cuts the y-axis.

   (a) $y = 4x + 6$ $\quad$ **(b)** $y = 3x - 2$ $\quad$ **(c)** $y = x + 5$
   (d) $y = 6x - 5$ $\quad$ **(e)** $y = 9x + 4$ $\quad$ **(f)** $y = 7x - 6$
   (g) $y = 3x - 1$ $\quad$ **(h)** $y = 7x + 2$ $\quad$ **(i)** $y = 5x - 3$

When the equation of a straight line is in the form
$\qquad y = mx + c$
• the gradient of the line is m
• the line cuts the y-axis at $(0,c)$.

The line $y = 6x + 2$ has gradient 6 and
$\qquad\qquad\qquad\qquad$ cuts the y-axis at $(0,2)$.

The line $y = 3x - 5$ has gradient 3 and
$\qquad\qquad\qquad\qquad$ cuts the y-axis at $(0, {}^-5)$.

The line $y = x + 7$ has gradient 1 and
$\qquad\qquad\qquad\qquad$ cuts the y-axis at $(0,7)$.

4 For the graph of each equation write:
   • the gradient
   • the coordinates of the point where it cuts the y-axis.

   (a) $y = 3x + 1$ $\quad$ **(b)** $y = 2x - 5$ $\quad$ **(c)** $y = 4x + 2$
   (d) $y = 5x + 9$ $\quad$ **(e)** $y = x - 6$ $\quad$ **(f)** $y = 7x + 4$
   (g) $y = x - 7$ $\quad$ **(h)** $y = 8x$ $\quad\quad$ **(i)** $y = x - 4$
   (j) $y = 2$ $\qquad\quad$ **(k)** $y = 3x$ $\quad\quad$ **(l)** $y = 7$

Finding equations

Tara is trying to find the equation of this straight line.

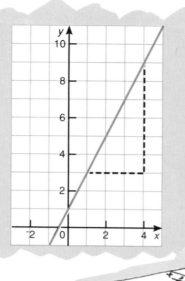

She chooses two points, (1,3) and (4,9), to calculate the gradient.

Gradient = distance up ÷ distance along
$$= 6 \div 3$$
$$= 2$$

so $m = 2$

The graph cuts the y-axis at the point (0,1)
so $c = 1$

Tara replaces m by 2 and c by 1 in the equation
$$y = mx + c$$
to give $y = 2x + 1$.

1 For each graph:
 • find the gradient of the line
 • find the point where the line cuts the y-axis
 • write the equation of the line.

(a)

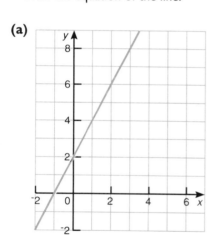

(b)

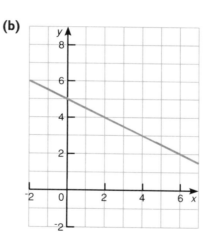

(c)

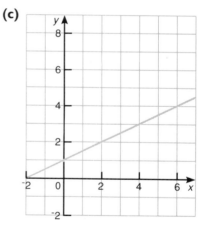

(d)

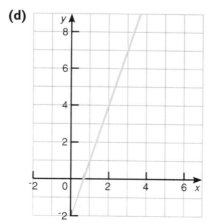

(e)

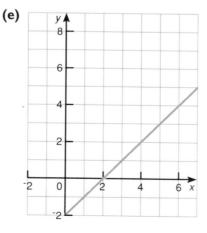

(f)

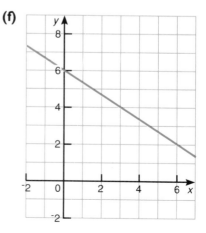

In an experiment, gas was heated in a cylinder containing a piston.
Paul recorded the distance the piston moved at different temperatures.

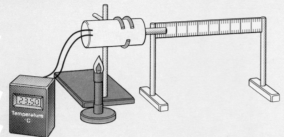

Temperature in °C (T)	20	30	40	50
Distance in mm (d)	20	25	30	35

He wanted to know if there was an equation linking d and T.

Paul drew a graph of the results.

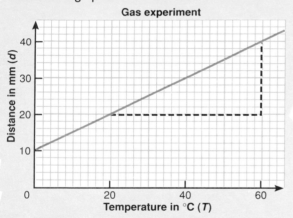

Gas experiment

As the graph is a straight line, the equation will be of the form $y = mx + c$, or in this case
$$d = mt + c.$$

Gradient = distance up ÷ distance along
$$= 20 \div 40$$
$$= 0.5$$

so $m = 0.5$

The line cuts the Distance axis at (0,10) so $c = 10$

Paul replaced m by 0.5 and c by 10 in the equation
$$d = mT + c$$
to give $d = 0.5T + 10$
where d is the distance in mm moved by the piston and T is the temperature in °C.

---

1 In another experiment Paul heated two metal bars and recorded their lengths at different temperatures. Draw a graph for each bar and find the equations of the lines.

Bar A

Temperature in °C (T)	20	40	60	80
Length in mm (l)	30	35	40	45

Bar B

Temperature in °C (T)	20	40	60	80
Length in mm (l)	14	18	22	26

2 At a test site the efficiency of new road surfaces is tested. From a speed of 10 m/s the brakes in a truck are applied and the speed is measured every second. The results for two surfaces are shown in the tables.

Surface A

Time in seconds (t)	0	1	2	3
Speed in m/s (s)	10	8	6	4

Surface B

Time in seconds (t)	0	1	2	3
Speed in m/s (s)	10	7.5	5	2.5

(a) Draw a graph for each surface and find the equations of the lines.

(b) Which surface is the most efficient? Give a reason for your answer.

1 Maria works in a pharmacy. She has identical boxes of pills. She found that 5 boxes plus a 30g weight is heavier than 3 boxes plus a 40g weight.
Write a statement about the weight of each box of pills.

2 This is a plan of Ailsa's lounge. It requires exactly 18 m^2 of carpet.

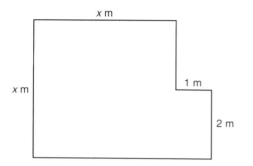

(a) Write an equation to model this situation.
(b) Solve your equation to find the value of x.

3 John is planning to build this access ramp.

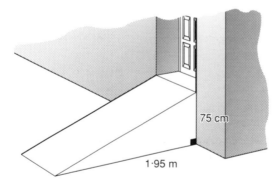

Local building regulations state that the gradient must be no more that 0·4. Would the ramp meet the building regulations? Explain your answer.

4 Alison has been offered a part-time job. She has to choose which method of payment she prefers.

Method 1   Method 2
w = 5h   w = 4h + 20

where w is the wage in £ and
      h is the time in hours.

(a) On the same diagram, draw graphs to show each method of payment.
(b) What advice would you give Alison?

5 These are two hydrocarbon molecules.

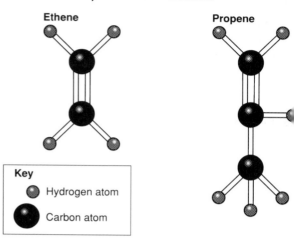

(a) Write, in simplest form, the ratio of hydrogen atoms to carbon atoms for each hydrocarbon.
(b) The mass of each hydrogen atom is 1 unit and of each carbon atom is 12 units.
   Write, in simplest form, the ratio of the mass of hydrogen to the mass of carbon for each hydrocarbon.
(c) What is the mass of carbon as a percentage of the total mass of each hydrocarbon?

6 The velocity of a particle can be calculated from the formula $v = \dfrac{s}{t}$

where v is the velocity in m/s
       s is the displacement in metres and
       t is the time in seconds.

(a) Calculate the velocity of the particle when:
   • s is 5 and t is 2·5
   • s is $2·3 \times 10^{-6}$ and t is $1·15 \times 10^{-19}$
(b) Rearrange the formula, making t the subject.
(c) Calculate the time taken by a particle to travel $6·5 \times 10^{7}$ m at a velocity of $2·5 \times 10^{12}$ m/s.

7 A Dutch businessman bought a Highland estate of 6400 hectares at £520 per hectare when the exchange rate was 3·21 guilders to the £. He sold the estate for £3 million when the exchange rate was 2·93 guilders to the £. Find, in guilders, the difference in the value of the estate.

8 Orange juice is sold in cans and cartons.

(a) Calculate the volume of each container.
   (Volume of a cylinder, $V = \pi r^2 h$)
(b) Which is the better value for money? Explain.
(c) This tray is used to transport cans or cartons.

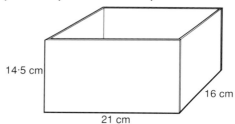

Calculate the maximum number of:
• cans   • cartons
which can be fitted into one layer on this tray.

9 A staff canteen offers the following menu.

Today's Menu		
First course	Second course	Third course
Soup	Fish + chips	Ice cream
	Steak pie	
Orange	Cottage pie	
juice	Lasagne	Lemon pie
	Curry	

Staff choose one item from each course.
(a) How many different meals is it possible to choose?
(b) What is the probability that a staff member will choose soup, fish and chips and ice cream?
(c) What is the probability that a staff member will choose fish and chips?

10 Johan is making this kite.

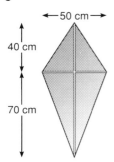

He has to fix twine around the perimeter. If he has 2·5 m of twine, does he have enough?

11 Helen cut circles from a square sheet of tin foil.

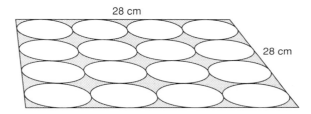

What area is left when the circles are removed?

12 Iain works as a joiner. He is paid an hourly rate of £4·50 for a basic 40 hour week.
Anne sells cars. She is not paid a basic wage, but earns a commission of 2·5% on all sales.
Last week Anne sold cars valued at £7500. Who was better paid that week?

13 Tom is surveying a building site.

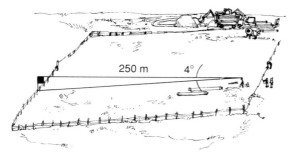

The angle of depression of the bottom of the site from the top is 4°. If the horizontal distance is 250 m, what is the drop in height?

This table and graph, from Wheeler's Garage, show that the cost of petrol is directly proportional to the number of litres.

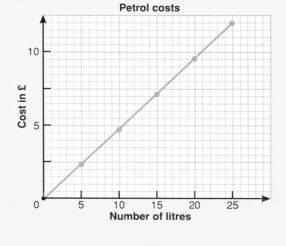

Petrol costs

Number of litres	5	10	15	20	25
Cost in £	2·40	4·80	7·20	9·60	12·00

As the number of litres doubles, the cost doubles; as the number of litres trebles the cost trebles.

The graph is a **straight line** through the **origin**.

It can be said that:
   the cost of petrol is **directly proportional** to the number of litres

or the cost of petrol **varies directly** as the number of litres.

These three graphs are also from Wheeler's Garage.

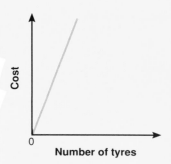

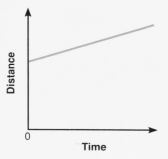

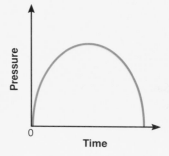

Since the graph is a straight line through the origin, **the cost varies directly as the number of tyres**.

Since the graph does not pass through the origin, **the distance does not vary directly as the time**.

Since the graph is not a straight line, **the pressure does not vary directly as the time**.

1 ▶ **Do Worksheet 15.**

2 Describe each graph.

(a)

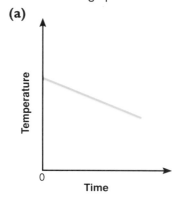

(b)

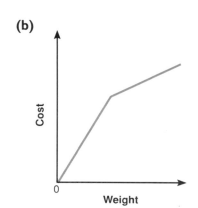

(c)

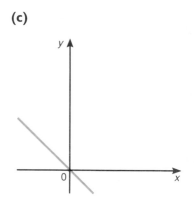

Catriona and Kauser have collected this data from
an electrical experiment and plotted it on a graph.

Voltage (volts)	2·2	3·4	5·6	8·2	10·8
Current (milliamps)	12·1	18·7	30·8	45·1	59·4

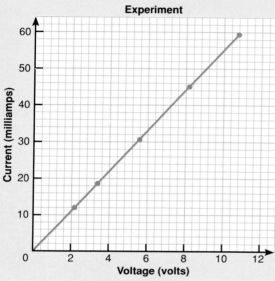

Experiment

Since the graph is a straight line through the origin,
the Current **varies directly** as the Voltage.

You need 2 mm graph paper.

1 Catriona claims that the following sets of data show
direct variation. For which sets of data is her claim
correct? Explain your answers.

(a)

Voltage (volts)	1·8	4·4	6·2	7·2
Current (milliamps)	4·5	11·0	15·5	18·0

(b)

Resistance (ohms)	2·4	3·4	4·4	5·4
Length (cm)	1·8	2·55	3·3	4·05

(c)

Days	1	2	3	4
Growth (cm)	0·5	0·75	0·85	0·9

(d)

Force (N)	2·5	4·5	5·5	7·5
Mass (g)	8	14·4	17·6	24

(e)

Time (s)	1	2	3	4
Distance (m)	2	8	18	32

(f)

Power (watts)	1·2	3	4·6	5
Current (milliamps)	10·2	25·5	39·1	42·5

(g)

Height (m)	2·20	2·30	2·40	2·50
Weight (kg)	40	50	60	65

Variation on a theme

In electrical circuits the voltage, V volts, always varies directly as the resistance, R ohms. These are the results from an experiment on a circuit.

Voltage (V)	Resistance (R)
8	2
12	3
16	4
20	5
24	6

From the table it can be seen that
Voltage (V) = 4 × Resistance (R)
$$V = 4R$$
4 is the **constant of variation**. It can be found by dividing any value of V by the corresponding value of R.

$8 \div 2 = 4, 12 \div 3 = 4, 16 \div 4 = 4 \ldots$

Using the formula $V = 4R$,

when $R = 9$, $V = 4 \times 9$ when $R = 20$, $V = 4 \times 20$
            = 36   **= 80**

1 These are the results from an experiment with another circuit.

Voltage (V)	Resistance (R)
10	2
15	3

  (a) Find the constant of variation.
  (b) Write the formula connecting V and R.
  (c) Find the voltage when the resistance is
      • 6 ohms • 10 ohms • 7·5 ohms.

2 These are the results from other circuits.
  For each: • find the constant of variation
             • write the formula connecting V and R
             • calculate V when R is 12
  (a) V is 6 when R is 2   **(b)** V is 7·5 when R is 5
  (c) V is 4 when R is 8   **(d)** V is 8 when R is 10

3 The tension, T newtons, in a spring varies directly as the extension, E cm. A tension of 25 newtons produces an extension of 10 cm.
What tension is required to produce an extension of 18 cm?

4 The cost, £C, of producing a newspaper varies directly as the number of pages, P.
A newspaper of 18 pages costs 15p. What is the cost of producing a 30 page newspaper?

5 The length, L inches, of rubber tubing in a bicycle tyre varies directly as the diameter, d inches, of the tyre. The length of tubing is 85 inches when the diameter is 27 inches. What is the length of tubing in a tyre of diameter 24 inches?

6 The force, F newtons, required to move a model boat varies directly as its acceleration, a ms^{-2}. If a force of 16 newtons is applied the acceleration will be 4 ms^{-2}. What is the acceleration when a force of 30 newtons is applied?

7 When a car is travelling at a constant speed, the distance, D miles, varies directly as the time taken, T hours. When the distance is 56 miles the time taken is 3 hours. Find the time taken to travel 31·5 miles.

The graph shows the volume and mass of copper.

From the graph, when the volume is 4 cm^3, the mass is 36 grams.
When the volume is 15 cm^3, the mass cannot be found from the graph. A formula connecting mass and volume has to be found.

Since the graph is a straight line through the origin, the volume varies directly as the mass.

The constant of variation = $36 \div 4 = 9$

The formula is $m = 9v$
where m is the mass in grams and
v is the volume in cm^3.
When $v = 15$, $m = 9 \times 15$
$= 135$

When the volume is 15 cm^3, the mass is **135 grams**.

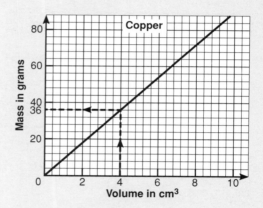

1 The graph shows the volume and mass of titanium.
   (a) Do the quantities vary directly? Explain your answer.
   (b) Use the graph to find the mass when the volume is 4 cm^3.
   (c) Calculate the constant of variation.
   (d) Write a formula.
   (e) Use your formula to find the mass of the metal when the volume is:
      • 20 cm^3 • 15 cm^3 • 9·3 cm^3 • 1·25 cm^3

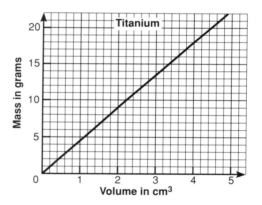

2 A car is being driven in fourth gear. The number of revolutions per minute of the engine, R, and the speed of the car, s, are shown on this graph.
   (a) Do the quantities vary directly? Explain your answer.
   (b) Use the graph to find R when the speed is 20 km/h.
   (c) Calculate the constant of variation.
   (d) Write a formula.
   (e) Use your formula to find R when the speed of the car is:
      • 55 km/h • 78 km/h • 113 km/h

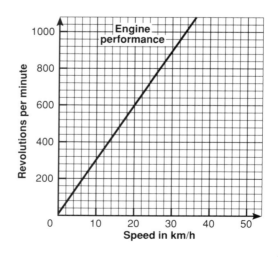

Catriona and Kauser measured the weight of circular discs of equal thickness. The table shows their results.

Diameter in cm	1	2	3	4	5
Weight in grams	8	32	72	128	200

Catriona drew this graph of diameter against weight.

Since the graph is not a straight line, the diameter does not vary directly as the weight.

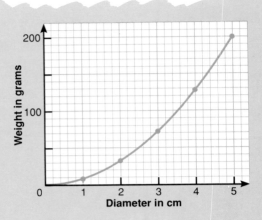

Kauser squared each diameter and made this table.

(Diameter in cm)^2	1	4	9	16	25
Weight in grams	8	32	72	128	200

She drew a graph of (diameter)^2 against weight.

Since the graph is a straight line through the origin, the weight varies directly as the (diameter)^2.

The constant of variation $= 32 \div 4 = 8$

The formula is **$w = 8d^2$** where w is the weight in grams and d is the diameter in cm.

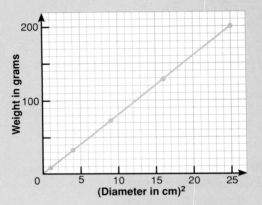

1 In another experiment Catriona and Kauser measured the length, d mm, and the weight, w grams, of several square pieces of metal with equal thickness. The table shows their results.

Length in mm (d)	5	10	15	20
Weight in grams (w)	250	1000	2250	4000

(a) Draw a graph of w against d.
(b) Does w vary directly as d? Explain your answer.
(c) Copy and complete the table.

(Length in mm)^2 (d^2)	25			
Weight in grams (w)	250	1000	2250	4000

(d) Draw a graph of w against d^2.
(e) Does w vary directly as d^2? Explain your answer.
(f) Calculate the constant of variation.
(g) Write a formula connecting w and d^2.
(h) Use the formula to find the value of w when d is: • 25 mm • 50 mm • 100 mm.

2 The data in this table was collected from an experiment using a pendulum.

Length in cm (l)	25	36	49	64	81	100
Time in s (t)	1	1·2	1·4	1·6	1·8	2

(a) Draw a graph of t against l.
(b) Does t vary directly as l?
(c) Make a table and draw a graph of t against l^2.
(d) Does t vary directly as l^2?
(e) Make a table and draw a graph of t against $\sqrt{l}$.
(f) Does t vary directly as $\sqrt{l}$?
(g) What is the constant of variation?
(h) Write the formula connecting t and $\sqrt{l}$.
(i) Use the formula to find t when l is:
• 0·16 m • 0·04 m • 1·21 m.

Checking an electrical circuit, Kauser has measured the current, I amps and the resistance, R ohms.
The table shows her results.

Resistance (R)	2	3	4	5
Current (I)	6	4	3	2·4

She drew this graph of I against R.
Since the graph is not a straight line, I does not vary directly as R.
Kauser then made this table, and drew a graph of I against $\frac{I}{R}$.

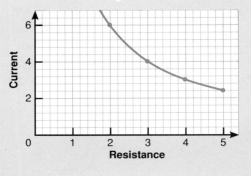

$\frac{I}{R}$	0·5	0·33	0·25	0·2
I	6	4	3	2·4

Since the graph is a straight line through the origin,
I varies directly as $\frac{I}{R}$.

The constant of variation $= 6 \div 0·5 = 12$

The formula is $I = 12 \times \frac{I}{R}$ or $I = \frac{12}{R}$ where I is the current in amps and R is the resistance in ohms.

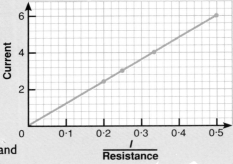

1 Kauser collected these results from a different circuit.

Resistance (R)	2	3	4	5
Current (I)	5	3·33	2·5	2

(a) Draw a graph of I against R. Does I vary directly as R? Explain your answer.

(b) Copy and complete the table.

$\frac{I}{R}$	0·5			
I	5	3·33	2·5	2

(c) Draw a graph of I against $\frac{I}{R}$. Does I vary directly as $\frac{I}{R}$?

(d) Find the constant of variation.

(e) Copy and complete:

The formula is $I = \dfrac{\square}{R}$ where I is the current in amps and R is the resistance in ohms.

(f) Find I when R is: • 10 • 20 • 50

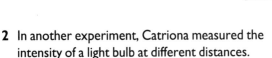

2 In another experiment, Catriona measured the intensity of a light bulb at different distances.
The table shows her results.

Distance (d)	1	2	3	4
Intensity (I)	64	16	7·11	4

(a) Draw a graph of I against d. Does I vary directly as d? Explain your answer.

(b) Copy and complete the table.

$\frac{I}{d^2}$		1	0·25	
I	64	16	7·11	4

(c) Draw a graph of I against $\frac{I}{d^2}$. Does I vary directly as $\frac{I}{d^2}$?

(d) Find the constant of variation.

(e) Copy and complete:

The formula is $I = \boxed{} \times \dfrac{I}{d^2}$ or $I = \dfrac{\square}{d^2}$
where I is the intensity of light and d is the distance from the bulb.

A variety of problems

The distance, D metres, that a stone falls when dropped varies directly as the square of the time, t seconds, from when the stone is dropped. After 2 seconds the stone has fallen 20 metres. How far will it have fallen after 4 seconds?

$D = kt^2$
$20 = k \times 2^2$
$20 = 4k$
$k = 5$

So $D = 5t^2$

When $t = 4$
$D = 5t^2$
$D = 5 \times 4^2$
$D = 80$

After 4 seconds the stone will have dropped **80 metres**.

1 The volume, V cm^3, of a cone of constant height varies directly as the square of the radius, r cm, of the base. A cone with volume 42 cm^3 has a base of radius 2 cm. What is the volume of a cone with a base radius of 4 cm?

2 The distance, D km, that can be seen from a cliff varies directly as the square root of the height, h m, above sea-level. At a height of 9 m, Amy can see 7·8 km. What distance can she see from a height of 16 m?

3 The speed, s m/s, that a train can safely travel round a curve varies directly as the square root of the radius, r metres, of the track. When the radius of the track is 64 metres, the safe speed is 16 m/s. Find the safe speed when the radius of the track is 144 metres.

4 The cost, £C, of square rugs varies directly as the square of their length, l metres. A rug of length 2 metres costs £40. What is the cost of a rug of length 2·5 metres?

5 A printer charges his photocopying according to the number of copies supplied. The charge, £C, varies directly as the square root of the number of copies, N. The charge for 100 copies is £1·50. What is the charge for 2500 copies?

6 The kinetic energy, K joules, of a roller coaster varies directly as the square of its speed, s m/s. A roller coaster travelling at 5 m/s has kinetic energy of 3125 joules. What is the kinetic energy of the roller coaster when it is travelling at a speed of 30 m/s?

Powerful numbers

Indices:
Calculation of a^n,
use of the x^y button

104

Many years ago a wise man was offered a reward. He asked for 1 grain of rice to be placed on the first square of a chessboard, 2 grains on the second, 4 grains on the third, 8 grains on the fourth and so on. How many grains of rice would be placed on the last square?

Square	1	2	3	4	5
Number of grains	1	2	4	8	16

$$16 = 2 \times 2 \times 2 \times 2 = 2^4$$
$$8 = 2 \times 2 \times 2 \quad = 2^3$$
$$4 = 2 \times 2 \quad\quad = 2^2$$
$$2 = 2 \quad\quad\quad = 2^1$$

• From the pattern $1 = 2^0$

Square	1	2	3	4	5
Number of grains	2^0	2^1	2^2	2^3	2^4

From the pattern in the table there would be **2^{63} grains of rice** on the last square of the chessboard.

2^5 is read as 2 to the power of 5.
2 is called the **base**.
5 is called the **index**.
Numbers written like this are in **index form**.

1 Express in index form:
   (a) $2 \times 2 \times 2 \times 2 \times 2$ (b) $5 \times 5 \times 5$
   (c) $4 \times 4 \times 4 \times 4 \times 4 \times 4$ (d) $r \times r \times r \times r$
   (e) $t \times t \times t \times t \times t \times t \times t \times t \times t$
   (f) $y \times y \times y \times y \times y \times y \times y$
   (g) $z \times z \times z \times z \times z \times z \times z \times z \times z \times z \times z$

2 Write in full:
   (a) 3^2 (b) 2^5 (c) 4^3 (d) 5^6
   (e) t^3 (f) v^9 (g) r^7 (h) s^{10}
   (i) 5^7 (j) g^1 (k) y^8 (l) a^{12}

3 Calculate the value of:
   (a) 4^3 (b) 8^2 (c) 6^3 (d) 2^6
   (e) 15^1 (f) 1^5 (g) 3^5 (h) 2^8
   (i) 3^6 (j) 4^4 (k) 7^4 (l) 6^5
   (m) 1^8 (n) 10^5 (o) 2^{10} (p) 13^1

4 Write:
   (a) 4 as a power of 2   (b) 9 as a power of 3
   (c) 16 as a power of 4   (d) 8 as a power of 2
   (e) 25 as a power of 5   (f) 125 as a power of 5.

To find the value of 3^5 using a calculator:

Enter **3**. Press **x^y** **5** **=** to give **243.**

$3^5 = 243$

5 Use your calculator to find:
   (a) 4^7 (b) 3^8 (c) 5^5 (d) 8^6
   (e) 6^8 (f) 10^7 (g) $2 \cdot 5^4$ (h) $1 \cdot 06^2$

6 Which number is larger:
   (a) 3^6 or 6^3 (b) 2^5 or 5^2 (c) 3^7 or 7^3
   (d) 4^6 or 6^4 (e) 4^8 or 8^4 (f) 5^6 or 6^5?

7 What is the highest power to which 2 can be raised before the calculator answer is expressed in standard form?

8 On the last square of the chessboard there were 2^{63} grains of rice. Express this in standard form.

9 Try to find 25^{75} using your calculator. Interpret the display.

▶ **Challenge**

10 (a) Find the value of:
      • 6^0 • 15^0 • 9^0 • 3^0
   (b) Repeat for another four numbers.
   (c) Write about what you have discovered.

105

Indices:
$a^m \times a^n = a^{m+n}$
$a^m \div a^n = a^{m-n}$
$(m > n)$

Indices rule

$$2^5 \times 2^2 = (2 \times 2 \times 2 \times 2 \times 2) \times (2 \times 2)$$
$$= 2 \times 2 \times 2 \times 2 \times 2 \times 2 \times 2$$
$$= 2^7$$
$$a^5 \times a^2 = (a \times a \times a \times a \times a) \times (a \times a)$$
$$= a \times a \times a \times a \times a \times a \times a$$
$$= a^7$$

1 Simplify

(a) $5^3 \times 5^7$ (b) $3^3 \times 3^6$ (c) $7^4 \times 7^5$

(d) $a^3 \times a^7$ (e) $p^4 \times p^8$ (f) $s^7 \times s^6$

2 Look at your answers to question **1**. What do you notice?

To **multiply** numbers with the same base, add the indices.

$$2^5 \times 2^2 = 2^{5+2} = 2^7$$
$$a^5 \times a^2 = a^{5+2} = a^7$$

In general, $a^m \times a^n = a^{m+n}$

3 Simplify:

(a) $6^5 \times 6^3$ (b) $3^9 \times 3^7$ (c) $8^3 \times 8^9$

(d) $9^5 \times 9^{10}$ (e) $10^6 \times 10^8$ (f) $7^8 \times 7^{12}$

(g) $u^5 \times u^{15}$ (h) $t^{17} \times t^6$ (i) $c^6 \times c^{14}$

(j) $c^6 \times c^8$ (k) $n^{12} \times n^9$ (l) $r^9 \times r^6$

$$2^5 \times 2^8 \times 2^4 = 2^{5+8+4} \qquad 6^7 \times 6^3 \times 6^{12} = 6^{7+3+12}$$
$$= 2^{17} \qquad\qquad\qquad = 6^{22}$$

4 Simplify:

(a) $7^8 \times 7^5 \times 7^4$ (b) $12^4 \times 12^9 \times 12^5$

(c) $17^7 \times 17^6 \times 17^5 \times 17^{12}$ (d) $3^9 \times 3^8 \times 3^2 \times 3$

$$2a^5 \times 3a^7 = (2 \times a^5) \times (3 \times a^7)$$
$$= 2 \times a^5 \times 3 \times a^7$$
$$= 2 \times 3 \times a^5 \times a^7$$
$$= 6 \times a^{12}$$
$$= 6a^{12}$$

5 Simplify:

(a) $3a^4 \times 5a^3$ (b) $4c^9 \times 2c^6$ (c) $4t^9 \times 7t^3$

(d) $6d^3 \times 4d^8$ (e) $3p^2 \times 5p^5$ (f) $4c^6 \times 7c^3$

$$2^5 \div 2^3 = (2 \times 2 \times 2 \times 2 \times 2) \div (2 \times 2 \times 2)$$
$$= 32 \div 8$$
$$= 4$$
$$= 2^2$$
$$2^5 \div 2^3 = 2^2$$
$$5^6 \div 5^3 = (5 \times 5 \times 5 \times 5 \times 5 \times 5) \div (5 \times 5 \times 5)$$
$$= 15\,625 \div 125$$
$$= 125$$
$$= 5^3$$
$$5^6 \div 5^3 = 5^3$$

6 Use the method above to simplify:

(a) $4^7 \div 4^5$ (b) $3^8 \div 3^5$

(c) $8^6 \div 8^5$ (d) $7^9 \div 7^7$

7 Look at your answers to question **6**. What do you notice?

To **divide** numbers with the same base, subtract the indices.

$$4^8 \div 4^3 = 4^{8-3} \qquad 7^{19} \div 7^{12} = 7^{19-12} \qquad t^8 \div t^3 = t^{8-3}$$
$$= 4^5 \qquad\qquad\qquad = 7^7 \qquad\qquad\qquad = t^5$$

In general, $a^m \div a^n = a^{m-n}$

8 Simplify:

(a) $5^7 \div 5^3$ (b) $9^8 \div 9^2$ (c) $7^6 \div 7^2$

(d) $6^{12} \div 6^5$ (e) $15^{17} \div 15^9$ (f) $9^4 \div 9^2$

(g) $v^6 \div v^2$ (h) $z^{19} \div z^5$ (i) $c^{16} \div c^3$

(j) $k^{25} \div k^{19}$ (k) $b^{16} \div b^5$ (l) $r^{30} \div r^{19}$

$a^m \div a^n = a^{m-n}$
$(m>n),$
$(a^m)^n = a^{mn},$
$(ab)^m = a^m b^m$

106

$$24c^7 \div c^5 = (24 \times c^7) \div c^5$$
$$= 24 \times c^7 \div c^5$$
$$= 24 \times c^{7-5}$$
$$= \mathbf{24c^2}$$

9 Simplify:
  (a) $12c^8 \div c^3$ **(b)** $14v^9 \div v^2$ **(c)** $15b^4 \div b^3$
  (d) $32k^6 \div k^2$ **(e)** $48f^{10} \div f^6$ **(f)** $30c^6 \div c^4$

$$24c^7 \div 3 = (24 \times c^7) \div 3$$
$$= 24 \times c^7 \div 3$$
$$= 24 \div 3 \times c^7$$
$$= \mathbf{8c^7}$$

10 Simplify:
  (a) $12c^8 \div 3$ **(b)** $14v^9 \div 7$ **(c)** $15b^4 \div 3$
  (d) $32k^6 \div 8$ **(e)** $48f^{10} \div 6$ **(f)** $30c^6 \div 6$

$$24c^7 \div 3c^5 \quad 24c^7 \div 3 = 8c^7$$
$$8c^7 \div c^5 = 8c^2$$
$$\mathbf{24c^7 \div 3c^5 = 8c^2}$$

11 Simplify:
  (a) $12c^8 \div 3c^3$ **(b)** $14v^9 \div 7v^2$ **(c)** $15b^4 \div 3b^3$
  (d) $32k^6 \div 8k^2$ **(e)** $48f^{10} \div 6f^6$ **(f)** $30c^6 \div 6c^4$
  (g) $35v^6 \div 7v^3$ **(h)** $56d^8 \div 8d^3$ **(i)** $42p^9 \div 6p^8$

$$7^5 \times 7^4 \div 7^6 = 7^{5+4-6} \qquad 8^3 \div 8^6 \times 8^7 = 8^{3-6+7}$$
$$= 7^3 \qquad\qquad\qquad = 8^4$$
$$s^8 \times s^9 \div s^4 = s^{8+9-4} \qquad b^2 \div b^5 \times b^9 = b^{2-5+9}$$
$$= s^{13} \qquad\qquad\qquad = b^6$$

12 Simplify:
  (a) $8^5 \div 8^3 \times 8^4$ **(b)** $4^5 \times 4^9 \div 4^8$
  (c) $12^9 \div 12^7 \times 12^6$ **(d)** $13^9 \div 13^{16} \times 13^{10}$
  (e) $h^{19} \div h^{13} \times h^7$ **(f)** $c^7 \div c^9 \times c^4$
  (g) $k^{18} \div k^5 \div k^8$ **(h)** $p^7 \div p^3 \times p^8 \div p^4$

$$(7^5)^3 = 7^5 \times 7^5 \times 7^5$$
$$= 7^{5+5+5}$$
$$= 7^{3 \times 5}$$
$$= \mathbf{7^{15}}$$

$$(y^7)^5 = y^7 \times y^7 \times y^7 \times y^7 \times y^7$$
$$= y^{7+7+7+7+7}$$
$$= y^{5 \times 7}$$
$$= \mathbf{y^{35}}$$

13 Use the method above to simplify:
  (a) $(4^7)^3$ **(b)** $(3^8)^5$ **(c)** $(8^6)^5$ **(d)** $(d^9)^6$

14 Look at your answers to question **13**.
    What do you notice?

To find a power of a number in index form,
multiply the indices.

$$(9^6)^8 = 9^{6 \times 8} \qquad (10^4)^7 = 10^{4 \times 7} \qquad (c^5)^6 = c^{5 \times 6}$$
$$= 9^{48} \qquad\qquad = 10^{28} \qquad\qquad = c^{30}$$

In general, $(a^m)^n = a^{mn}$

15 Simplify:
  (a) $(6^7)^5$ **(b)** $(8^5)^8$ **(c)** $(12^7)^3$ **(d)** $(9^8)^5$
  (e) $(15^6)^7$ **(f)** $(11^4)^9$ **(g)** $(18^3)^9$ **(h)** $(10^8)^4$
  (i) $(c^6)^5$ **(j)** $(t^4)^8$ **(k)** $(y^7)^5$ **(l)** $(b^9)^6$

$$(3v)^4 = 3v \times 3v \times 3v \times 3v$$
$$= 3 \times 3 \times 3 \times 3 \times v \times v \times v \times v$$
$$= 3^4 \times v^4$$
$$= \mathbf{81v^4}$$

16 Simplify:
  (a) $(6h)^3$ **(b)** $(5f)^4$ **(c)** $(7k)^2$ **(d)** $(4k)^5$
  (e) $(3k)^6$ **(f)** $(9r)^2$ **(g)** $(2u)^6$ **(h)** $(2f)^7$

In general, $(ab)^n = a^n b^n$

$$(6d)^5 = 6^5 d^5 \qquad (6s)^7 = 6^7 s^7 \qquad (9h)^5 = 9^5 h^5$$

17 In the same way, express as a product:
  (a) $(8f)^9$ **(b)** $(7j)^6$ **(c)** $(12t)^{17}$ **(d)** $(15r)^9$
  (e) $(15f)^4$ **(f)** $(23y)^7$ **(g)** $(18b)^6$ **(h)** $(16s)^{14}$

Since $4^2 = 4 \times 4 = 16$ then $\sqrt{16} = 4$

> read as the square root of 16

Since $4^3 = 4 \times 4 \times 4 = 64$ then $\sqrt[3]{64} = 4$

> read as the cube root of 64

Since $4^4 = 4 \times 4 \times 4 \times 4 = 256$ then $\sqrt[4]{256} = 4$

> read as the fourth root of 256

Round all answers to 2 decimal places where necessary.

1 Without using a calculator, find:

(a) $\sqrt{16}$ (b) $\sqrt{25}$ (c) $\sqrt{64}$ (d) $\sqrt{100}$

(e) $\sqrt[3]{8}$ (f) $\sqrt[3]{27}$ (g) $\sqrt[3]{1}$ (h) $\sqrt[3]{0}$

(i) $\sqrt[4]{16}$ (j) $\sqrt[4]{81}$ (k) $\sqrt[4]{1}$ (l) $\sqrt[4]{0}$

Evaluate $\sqrt[3]{10}$ using a calculator.

Enter **10.** Press **$x\sqrt{y}$** **3** **=**

to give  `2.1544347`

$\sqrt[3]{10} = 2\cdot15$ to 2 decimal places.

Evaluate $\sqrt[4]{10}$ using a calculator.

Enter **10.** Press **$x\sqrt{y}$** **4** **=**

to give `1.7782794`

$\sqrt[4]{10} = 1\cdot78$ to 2 decimal places.

2 Use a calculator to evaluate:

(a) $\sqrt[3]{8\cdot5}$ (b) $\sqrt[3]{25}$ (c) $\sqrt[3]{12}$ (d) $\sqrt[3]{238}$

(e) $\sqrt[3]{7\cdot65}$ (f) $\sqrt[3]{0\cdot125}$ (g) $\sqrt[3]{0\cdot008}$ (h) $\sqrt[4]{1\cdot4}$

(i) $\sqrt[4]{100}$ (j) $\sqrt[4]{15\cdot8}$ (k) $\sqrt[4]{361}$ (l) $\sqrt[4]{11}$

3 Find the edge length of each cube.

(a) 8 cm³   (b) 12 cm³

(c) 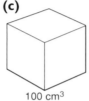 100 cm³   (d) 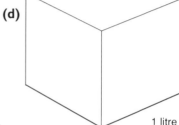 1 litre

---

● **Remember**

$$a^2 \times a^3 = a^{2+3} = a^5$$

So $a^{\frac{1}{2}} \times a^{\frac{1}{2}} = a^{\frac{1}{2}+\frac{1}{2}} = a^1 = a$

Also $\sqrt{a} \times \sqrt{a} = a$

So $a^{\frac{1}{2}}$ must be the same as $\sqrt{a}$.

$$a^{\frac{1}{2}} = \sqrt{a}$$

$$9^{\frac{1}{2}} = \sqrt{9} = 3$$

$$6\cdot25^{\frac{1}{2}} = \sqrt{6\cdot25} = 2\cdot5$$

---

4 Without using a calculator, evaluate:

(a) $16^{\frac{1}{2}}$ (b) $25^{\frac{1}{2}}$ (c) $64^{\frac{1}{2}}$ (d) $100^{\frac{1}{2}}$

(e) $81^{\frac{1}{2}}$ (f) $49^{\frac{1}{2}}$ (g) $1^{\frac{1}{2}}$ (h) $0^{\frac{1}{2}}$

5 Use a calculator to evaluate:

(a) $1\cdot25^{\frac{1}{2}}$ (b) $8\cdot3^{\frac{1}{2}}$ (c) $7\cdot6^{\frac{1}{2}}$ (d) $67\cdot9^{\frac{1}{2}}$

(e) $101^{\frac{1}{2}}$ (f) $135^{\frac{1}{2}}$ (g) $0\cdot25^{\frac{1}{2}}$ (h) $0\cdot72^{\frac{1}{2}}$

Evaluate $10^{\frac{1}{3}}$ to 2 decimal places using a calculator

Enter **10** Press **ˣ√y** **3** **=**

to give **2.1544347**

$\sqrt[3]{10}$ or $10^{\frac{1}{3}}$ is **2·15** to 2 decimal places.

9 Use a calculator to evaluate:

(a) $7·5^{\frac{1}{3}}$ (b) $\sqrt[3]{29}$ (c) $14^{\frac{1}{3}}$ (d) $\sqrt[3]{461}$

(e) $\sqrt[3]{25·7}$ (f) $0·392^{\frac{1}{3}}$ (g) $0·001^{\frac{1}{3}}$ (h) $10·4^{\frac{1}{4}}$

(i) $198^{\frac{1}{4}}$ (j) $\sqrt[4]{25·8}$ (k) $1340^{\frac{1}{4}}$ (l) $\sqrt[4]{18}$

(m) $\sqrt[4]{16}$ (n) $83·2^{\frac{1}{4}}$ (o) $\sqrt[3]{999}$ (p) $\sqrt[4]{999}$

▼ Challenge

10 The radius of a sphere is given by the formula:

$$r = \sqrt[3]{\frac{3V}{4\pi}}$$

where r is the radius in cm and
     V is the volume in cm^3
Calculate the radius of each sphere.

(a) 6500 cm^3 (b) 2140 cm^3

(c) 113 000 cm^3 (d) 268 cm^3

(e) 14 100 cm^3 (f) 7240 cm^3

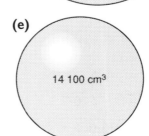

6 Copy and complete:

$a \times a \times a = a^{1+1+1} = a^3$

so $a^{\frac{1}{3}} \times a^{\frac{1}{3}} \times a^{\frac{1}{3}} = a^{\frac{1}{3} + \square + \square} = a^{\square} = a$

also $\sqrt[3]{a} \times \sqrt[3]{a} \times \sqrt[3]{a} = a$

so $a^{\frac{1}{3}}$ must be the same as $\sqrt[\square]{a}$.

$a^{\frac{1}{3}} = \sqrt[\square]{a}$

7 Copy and complete:

$a \times a \times a \times a = a^{1+1+1+1} = a^4$

so $a^{\frac{1}{4}} \times a^{\frac{1}{4}} \times a^{\frac{1}{4}} \times a^{\frac{1}{4}}$

$\qquad = a^{\frac{1}{4} + \square + \square + \square} = a^{\square} = a$

also $\sqrt[4]{a} \times \sqrt[4]{a} \times \sqrt[4]{a} \times \sqrt[4]{a} = a$

so $a^{\frac{1}{4}}$ must be the same as $\sqrt[\square]{a}$.

$a^{\frac{1}{4}} = \sqrt[\square]{a}$

$a^{\frac{1}{2}} = $ means $\sqrt{a}$

$a^{\frac{1}{3}} = $ means $\sqrt[3]{a}$

$a^{\frac{1}{4}} = $ means $\sqrt[4]{a}$

8 Without using a calculator, evaluate:

(a) $8^{\frac{1}{3}}$ (b) $27^{\frac{1}{3}}$ (c) $64^{\frac{1}{3}}$ (d) $1000^{\frac{1}{3}}$

(e) $16^{\frac{1}{4}}$ (f) $81^{\frac{1}{4}}$ (g) $0^{\frac{1}{3}}$ (h) $1^{\frac{1}{3}}$

(i) $36^{\frac{1}{2}}$ (j) $125^{\frac{1}{3}}$ (k) $121^{\frac{1}{2}}$ (l) $1^{\frac{1}{4}}$

The times they are a-changing

The Russian method of multiplication

This method of multiplication, **based on multiplying and dividing by 2**, is thought to have been developed by Russian peasants.

To multiply 37 by 22

```
37 ×  22
18 ×  44
 9 ×  88
 4 × 176
 2 × 352
 1 × 704    and     704
                      88
                  +   22
                     814
```

37 × 22 = 814

To multiply 27 by 65

```
27 ×   65
13 ×  130
 6 ×  260
 3 ×  520
 1 × 1040    and    1040
                     520
                     130
                  +   65
                     1755
```

27 × 65 = 1755

The Gelosia method of multiplication

Gelosia is an Italian word meaning grid or lattice. The use of grids or lattices for multiplication was popular in the 15th and 16th centuries.
This method uses simple multiplication then addition along diagonals.

To multiply 416 by 237:

	4	1	6	
0	0/8	0/2	1/2	2
9	1/2	0/3	1/8	3
8	2/8	0/7	4/2	7
	5	9	2	

To multiply 315 by 637:

	3	1	5	
2	1/8	0/6	3/0	6
0	0/9	0/3	1/5	3
0	2/1	0/7	3/5	7
	6	5	5	

416 × 237 = 98 592   **315 × 637 = 200 655**

---

1 (a) Use the Russian method to multiply:
- 21 × 43
- 23 × 22
- 46 × 115
- 32 × 245

(b) Use a calculator to check your answers.

2 Write a report explaining the Russian method of multiplcation.

3 (a) Use the Gelosia method to multiply:
- 156 × 642
- 236 × 531
- 425 × 63
- 1425 × 2476

(b) Use a calculator to check your answers.

4 Write a report explaining the Gelosia method of multiplication.

Sacha bought one Minty and two Snackers for 80p.
This can be written as **x + 2y = 80**

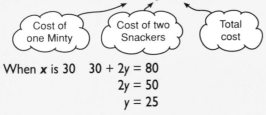

| Cost of one Minty | Cost of two Snackers | Total cost |

When **x** is 30

$$30 + 2y = 80$$
$$2y = 50$$
$$y = 25$$

If a Minty costs **30p** then a Snacker costs **25p**.

I Find the cost of a Snacker if a Minty costs:
   (a) 10p   **(b)** 50p

2 Find the cost of a Minty if a Snacker costs:
   (a) 20p   **(b)** 30p

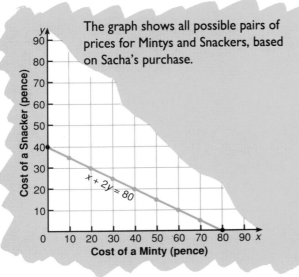

The graph shows all possible pairs of prices for Mintys and Snackers, based on Sacha's purchase.

3 Check that your answers for questions **I** and **2** lie on the graph.

4 Use the graph to find the cost of a Snacker if a Minty costs: **(a)** 24p   **(b)** 38p

5 Use the graph to find the cost of a Minty if a Snacker costs: **(a)** 12p   **(b)** 24p

Lee bought three Mintys and one Snacker for 90p.
This can be written as **3x + y = 90**

By finding three possible pairs of prices a graph can be drawn which shows all possible pairs of prices.

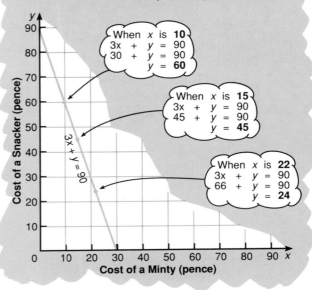

When x is **10**
$$3x + y = 90$$
$$30 + y = 90$$
$$y = 60$$

When x is **15**
$$3x + y = 90$$
$$45 + y = 90$$
$$y = 45$$

When x is **22**
$$3x + y = 90$$
$$66 + y = 90$$
$$y = 24$$

6 Use the graph to find the cost of a Snacker if a Minty costs: **(a)** 20p   **(b)** 12p

7 Use the graph to find the cost of a Minty if a Snacker costs: **(a)** 42p   **(b)** 78p

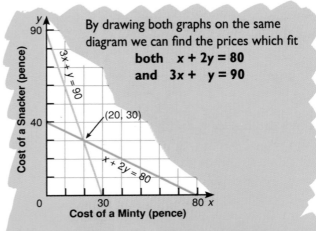

By drawing both graphs on the same diagram we can find the prices which fit
   both   **x + 2y = 80**
   and   **3x + y = 90**

(20, 30)

A Minty costs **20p** and a Snacker costs **30p**.

x + 2y = 80 and **3x + y = 90**
are called **simultaneous equations**.

There is **one** solution which fits **both** equations.

A graphic illustration

One adult with four children paid £25 to go to the meeting.

Two adults with one child paid £22.

We can write: $x + 4y = 25$ for 1 adult and 4 children

and $2x + y = 22$ for 2 adults and 1 child.

At Top Sports

Brenda bought 3 running vests and 2 pairs of shorts for £37.

Azil bought 2 running vests and 5 pairs of shorts for £43.

We can write:

$3x + 2y = 37$ for 3 vests and 2 pairs of shorts.

$2x + 5y = 43$ for 2 vests and 5 pairs of shorts.

1

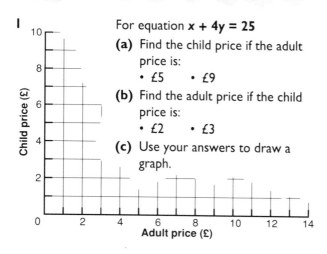

For equation $x + 4y = 25$

(a) Find the child price if the adult price is:
• £5   • £9

(b) Find the adult price if the child price is:
• £2   • £3

(c) Use your answers to draw a graph.

4

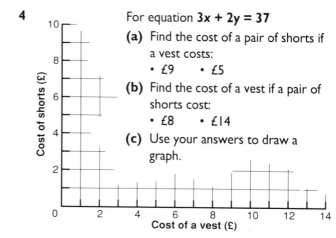

For equation $3x + 2y = 37$

(a) Find the cost of a pair of shorts if a vest costs:
• £9   • £5

(b) Find the cost of a vest if a pair of shorts cost:
• £8   • £14

(c) Use your answers to draw a graph.

2 For equation $2x + y = 22$

(a) Find the child price if the adult price is:
• £10   • £9

(b) Find the adult price if the child price is:
• £8   • £6

(c) Draw the graph on the same diagram as question **1(c)**.

3 (a) Write the coordinates of the point where the two graphs intersect.

(b) What is the cost for: • an adult   • a child?

5 For equation $2x + 5y = 43$

(a) Find the cost of a pair of shorts if a vest costs:
• £14   • £4

(b) Find the cost of a vest if a pair of shorts costs:
• £5   • £1

(c) Draw the graph on the same diagram as question **4(c)**.

6 (a) Write the coordinates of the point where the two graphs intersect.

(b) What is the cost of:
• a vest   • a pair of shorts?

To solve the simultaneous equations
$$x + y = 5$$
$$x + 3y = 7$$

- find three points which fit $x + y = 5$
  (0, 5), (2, 3), (5, 0)

- draw the graph of
  $x + y = 5$

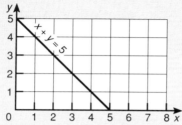

- find three points which fit $x + 3y = 7$
  (1, 2), (4, 1), (7, 0)

- on the same
  diagram draw
  the graph of
  $x + 3y = 7$

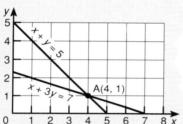

- find the point of intersection (4, 1)

The solution is $x = 4$ and $y = 1$.

The sum of two numbers is 13 and their difference is 3.
Call the numbers x and y. Then
$$x + y = 13$$
$$x - y = 3$$
(0, 13), (3, 10) and (13, 0)   lie on $x + y = 13$

(3, 0), (5, 2) and (10, 7)   lie on $x - y = 3$

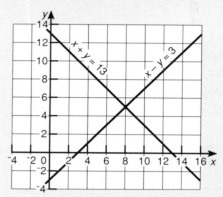

The point of intersection is (8, 5).
The numbers are **8** and **5**.

For each of the following problems:
- call the unknown numbers x and y
- form two equations
- solve the simultaneous equations
- write the solution to the problem.

---

1 To solve the simultaneous equations
$$x + y = 10$$
$$2x + y = 14$$

(a) Copy and complete for $x + y = 10$:
(0, ☐), (5, ☐), (10, ☐)

(b) Draw the graph of $x + y = 10$

(c) Copy and complete for $2x + y = 14$:
(0, ☐), (2, ☐), (6, ☐)

(d) On the same diagram draw the graph of
$2x + y = 14$

(e) Find the point of intersection and write the solution.

2 Solve each pair of simultaneous equations.
(a) $x + y = 12$ **(b)** $2x + y = 10$
  $3x + y = 14$ $x + 2y = 8$
(c) $x + y = 4$ **(d)** $2x + y = 8$
  $x + 3y = 8$ $3x + 2y = 14$
(e) $x + y = 7$ **(f)** $x + 5y = 13$
  $y = 5$ $x + y = 5$

3 The sum of two whole numbers is 19 and their difference is 9. Find the numbers.

4 The total cost of two books is £16 and the difference in their cost is £2. Find the cost of each book.

5 The sum of two angles is 90°.
One angle is 60° more than the other.
Find the size of each angle.

6 A sack of potatoes and a bag of onions together weigh 30 kg. They differ in weight by 20 kg.
Find the weight of a sack of potatoes.

7 In Super Sounds Jill sold a CD and a tape for £20.
Billy sold two CDs and a tape of the same album for £32.
Find the cost of the tape.

Ralph works in Nardoni's café.

Ralph charges £3·20 for one coffee and four teas.
He charges £2 for one coffee and two teas.

We can write two equations

$$c + 4t = 320$$
$$c + 2t = 200$$

Subtracting eliminates c
$$2t = 120$$
$$t = 60$$

Substitute 60 for t in
$$c + 4t = 320$$
$$c + 240 = 320$$
$$c = 80$$

A **tea** costs **60p** and a **coffee** costs **80p**.

1 Four cream cakes and a bun cost £4·50.
Three cream cakes and a bun cost £3·55.
• Using c pence as the cost of a cream cake and
  b pence as the cost of a bun, write two equations.
• Subtract equations to find c.
• Substitute to find b.

2

Nardoni's
SUNSHINE SUNDAES
FIVE SCOOPS £3·35
WITH FRUIT
THREE SCOOPS £2·25
WITH FRUIT

(a) Using i pence as the cost of one scoop of ice
cream and f as the cost of fruit, write two
equations for this menu.
(b) Subtract equations to find i.
(c) Substitute to find f.

3 For each pair of simultaneous equations:
• copy the equations
• subtract
• find x and y.

(a) $x + 3y = 8$
  $x + y = 6$

(b) $x + 5y = 22$
  $x + 2y = 10$

(c) $2x + y = 11$
  $x + y = 7$

(d) $3x + 4y = 31$
  $2x + 4y = 30$

(e) $7x + 4y = 30$
  $5x + 4y = 26$

(f) $5x + 8y = 43$
  $5x + 2y = 37$

(g) $3x + 2y = 33$
  $3x + 4y = 51$

(h) $5x + 7y = 17$
  $2x + 7y = 11$

To solve
$$2x + 4y = 34$$
$$3x - 4y = 1$$

Adding eliminates y
$$5x = 35$$
$$x = 7$$

Substitute 7 for x in
$$2x + 4y = 34$$
$$14 + 4y = 34$$
$$4y = 20$$
$$y = 5$$

The solution is $x = 7$ and $y = 5$.

4 For each pair of simultaneous equations:
• copy the equations
• add
• find x and y.

(a) $2x + 5y = 20$
  $3x - 5y = 5$

(b) $3x + 2y = 14$
  $2x - 2y = 6$

(c) $2x + 3y = 18$
  $x - 3y = 0$

(d) $6x + 3y = 18$
  $4x - 3y = 2$

(e) $y + 6x = 10$
  $3y - 6x = 6$

(f) $6y + x = 7$
  $2y - x = 1$

(g) $2x + 3y = 22$
  $4x - 3y = 26$

(h) $4x + y = 48$
  $7x - y = 73$

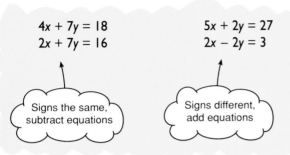

$4x + 7y = 18$
$2x + 7y = 16$

$5x + 2y = 27$
$2x - 2y = 3$

Signs the same, subtract equations

Signs different, add equations

1 Add or subtract each pair of simultaneous equations to find x and y.

(a) $2x + 3y = 19$
$\quad\ \ x + 3y = 17$

(b) $3x + 5y = 25$
$\quad\ \ 3x + 3y = 21$

(c) $4x - 5y = {}^-13$
$\quad\ \ 2x + 5y = 1$

(d) $7x + 2y = 27$
$\quad\ \ 5x - 2y = 9$

(e) $3x + 2y = {}^-1$
$\quad\ \ 5x - 2y = 9$

(f) $3x + 4y = 23$
$\quad\ \ 3x + \ y = 17$

(g) ${}^-3x + 4y = 7$
$\quad\ \ 3x + \ y = {}^-2$

(h) $2x + \ y = 13$
$\quad\ {}^-2x + 3y = 15$

(i) $4x + 5y = 50$
$\quad\ \ x + 5y = 20$

(j) $7x - 2y = 3$
$\quad\ 2x + 2y = 24$

For each of the following problems:
• write two equations
• solve by adding or subtracting.

2 A cone plus two scoops of ice cream costs 85p.
A cone plus one scoop costs 50p.
How much is a scoop of ice cream?

3 The length and breadth of a rectangle add to give 76 cm. The length is 24 cm longer than the breadth. What is the length of the rectangle?

4 The sum of two numbers is 63 and the difference between them is 13. What are the numbers?

5 Five Bix bars and two Sting bars cost £5·45.
Three Bix bars and two Sting bars cost £3·75.
How much is a Bix bar?

6 At the swimming club, membership for four adults and two children is £38.
Two adults and two children pay £22.
How much is an adult membership?

7 Lucy is a decorator. She bought six tins of white paint and three of blue. This cost her £81·60.
Four tins of white and three of blue cost £64·20.
How much is a tin of blue paint?

Balancing up

To solve
$$x + 4y = 31$$
$$2x + 3y = 27$$

Multiply the first equation by 2
$$2x + 8y = 62$$
$$2x + 3y = 27$$

Subtracting eliminates x
$$5y = 35$$
$$y = 7$$

Substitute 7 for y in
$$x + 4y = 31$$
$$x + 28 = 31$$
$$x = 3$$

The solution is $x = 3$ and $y = 7$.

To solve
$$3x + 3y = 30$$
$$2x - y = 2$$

Multiply the second equation by 3
$$3x + 3y = 30$$
$$6x - 3y = 6$$

Adding eliminates y
$$9x = 36$$
$$x = 4$$

Substitute 4 for x in
$$3x + 3y = 30$$
$$12 + 3y = 30$$
$$3y = 18$$
$$y = 6$$

The solution is $x = 4$ and $y = 6$.

1 For each pair of simultaneous equations:
- multiply one equation
- subtract
- find x and y.

(a) $x + 2y = 5$
$2x + 3y = 9$

(b) $5x + 3y = 22$
$2x + 6y = 4$

(c) $7x + 4y = 19$
$3x + 2y = 9$

(d) $7x + y = 10$
$3x + 2y = 9$

(e) $x + y = 0$
$4x + 3y = 3$

(f) $3x + 4y = {}^-7$
$2x + y = {}^-3$

(g) $7x + 4y = 1$
$5x + 2y = {}^-1$

(h) $2x + 3y = 5$
$x + y = 2$

For each of the following problems:
- write two equations
- multiply and solve.

2 At the theatre six stalls tickets and two balcony tickets cost £85.
Four stalls and one balcony ticket costs £54.
How much is a ticket for the stalls?

3 Three melons and two pineapples cost £8·70. One melon and four pineapples cost £6·40.
How much is a melon?

4 Five bags of sugar and two of coffee weigh a total of 11 kg. Two sugar and four coffee weigh 6 kg.
Find the weight of one bag of coffee.

5 For each pair of simultaneous equations:
- multiply one equation
- add
- find x and y.

(a) $5x - 2y = 16$
$x + y = 6$

(b) $3x + 4y = 29$
$2x - y = 1$

(c) $7x + 2y = 18$
$3x - y = 4$

(d) $11x + 4y = 7$
$2x - y = 3$

(e) $3x + 2y = 6$
$x - y = 2$

(f) $3x - 4y = 10$
$x + y = 1$

(g) $5x - 3y = 32$
$2x + 6y = 20$

(h) $6x + 2y = 38$
$2x - 10y = {}^-94$

6 Solve each pair of simultaneous equations.

(a) $3x + 2y = 8$
$x + 2y = 4$

(b) $5x + 2y = 27$
$x - 2y = 3$

(c) $3x + 8y = 6$
$3x - 4y = 6$

(d) $x + y = 10$
$x - y = 4$

(e) $5x + y = 30$
$3x - 4y = 41$

(f) $3x - 4y = 4$
$8x + y = 26$

(g) $2x + 3y = 19$
$x + 3y = 17$

(h) $5x + 2y = 11$
$2x + y = 5$

1

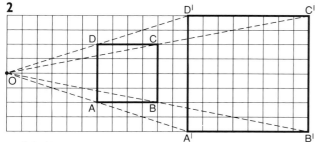

(a) Write the lengths of:
- OA and OA^1 • OB and OB^1
- OC and OC^1 • OD and OD^1

(b) Write the lengths of:
- AB and A^{1}B^1 • BC and B^{1}C^1
- CD and C^{1}D^1 • DA and D^{1}A^1

(c) What is the scale factor for the enlargement from ABCD to A^{1}B^{1}C^{1}D^1?

2

(a) Write the lengths of:
- OA and OA^1 • OB and OB^1
- OC and OC^1 • OD and OD^1

(b) Write the lengths of:
- AB and A^{1}B^1 • BC and B^{1}C^1
- CD and C^{1}D^1 • DA and D^{1}A^1

(c) What is the scale factor for the enlargement from ABCD to A^{1}B^{1}C^{1}D^1?

In both enlargements above:
- A^1, B^1, C^1 and D^1 are **images** of A, B, C and D
- for a scale factor of **2**, the distance from O to a point is **doubled** to find its image
- for a scale factor of **2**, the length of side of the image square is **twice** the length of side of the original square
- O is the **centre of dilatation**
- a point, its image and the centre of dilatation lie in a straight line.

3 ▶ Do Worksheet 16.

4

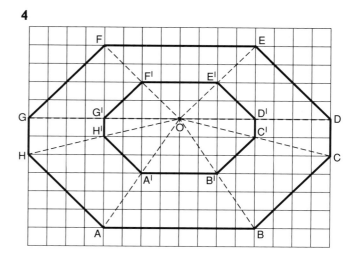

(a) Write the lengths of:
- OA and OA^1 • AB and A^{1}B^1

(b) What is the scale factor for this reduction?

5 ▶ Do Worksheet 17.

6

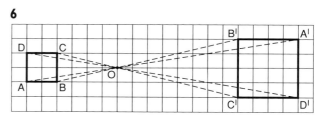

Write the lengths of:
- OA and OA^1 • AB and A^{1}B^1

The dilatation above has a scale factor of ⁻2.
A negative scale factor positions the image on the **opposite** side of the centre from the original shape.

7 ▶ Do Worksheet 18.

● **Remember**

For angle $a°$

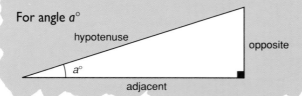

I For angle $a°$ in each triangle name:
  • the hypotenuse   • the opposite side
  • the adjacent side.

(a)   **(b)**   **(c)**

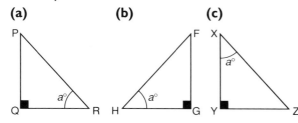

● **Remember**

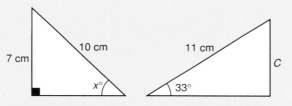

$$\sin x° = \frac{\text{opp}}{\text{hyp}} \qquad \sin 33° = \frac{\text{opp}}{\text{hyp}}$$

$$\sin x° = \frac{7}{10} = 0·7 \qquad \sin 33° = \frac{c}{11}$$

$$x° = 44·427004 \qquad 0·545 = \frac{c}{11}$$

$x°$ is 44·4° to I dp $11 \times 0·545 = c$

$$c = 5·995$$

c is 6·0 cm to I dp

2 Calculate the marked side or angle in each triangle.

(a)   **(b)**

(c)   **(d)**

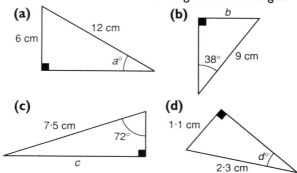

● **Remember**

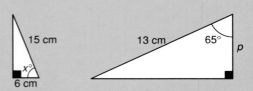

$$\cos x° = \frac{\text{adj}}{\text{hyp}} \qquad \cos 65° = \frac{\text{adj}}{\text{hyp}}$$

$$\cos x° = \frac{6}{15} = 0·4 \qquad 0·423 = \frac{p}{13}$$

$$x° = 66·421821 \qquad 13 \times 0·423 = p$$

$x°$ is 66·4° to I dp $p = 5·499$

p is 5·5 cm to I dp

3 Calculate x in each triangle.

(a)   **(b)**   **(c)**

(d)

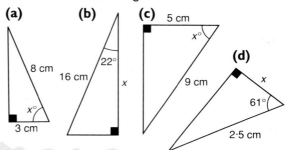

● **Remember**

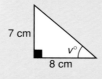   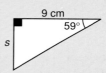

$$\tan v° = \frac{\text{opp}}{\text{adj}} \qquad \tan 59° = \frac{\text{opp}}{\text{adj}}$$

$$\tan v° = \frac{7}{8} = 0·875 \qquad \tan 59° = \frac{s}{9}$$

$$v° = 41·185925 \qquad 1·664 = \frac{s}{9}$$

$v°$ is 41·2° to I dp $9 \times 1·664 = s$

$$s = 14·976$$

s is 15·0 cm to I dp

4 Calculate x in each triangle.

(a)   **(b)**

● Remember

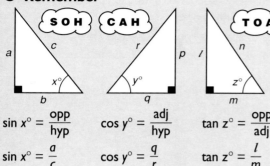

SOH   CAH   TOA

$$\sin x° = \frac{opp}{hyp} \qquad \cos y° = \frac{adj}{hyp} \qquad \tan z° = \frac{opp}{adj}$$

$$\sin x° = \frac{a}{c} \qquad \cos y° = \frac{q}{r} \qquad \tan z° = \frac{l}{m}$$

1 Calculate the value of *x* in each triangle.

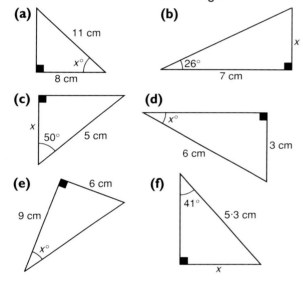

(a) 11 cm, *x*°, 8 cm

(b) *x*, 26°, 7 cm

(c) *x*, 50°, 5 cm

(d) *x*°, 6 cm, 3 cm

(e) 6 cm, 9 cm, *x*°

(f) 41°, 5·3 cm, *x*

2 A 5 m ladder rests against a wall.
The foot of the ladder is 1·8 m from the wall.

(a) Make a sketch marking in lengths.

(b) Find the angle between the ladder and the ground.

3 Chloe has to calculate the width of the river.
Use the information in the diagram to find *w*.

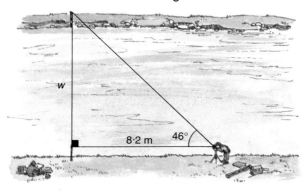

w, 8·2 m, 46°

4 Find the height of each flagpole.

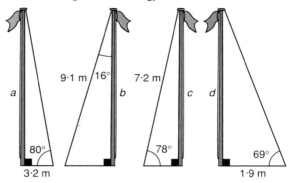

a, 80°, 3·2 m; 9·1 m, 16°, *b*; 7·2 m, 78°, *c*; *d*, 69°, 1·9 m

5 Calculate the angle of elevation of the tower.

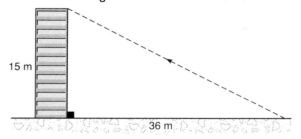

15 m, 36 m

6 The guy rope for this tent pole is 2·9 m long.
It makes an angle of 40° with the ground.
Calculate the distance from the pole to the
bottom of the rope.

7 The end of the seesaw
touches the ground 2·5 m
from the central support.
The support is 1·2 m high.
Find the angle between the
seesaw and the ground.

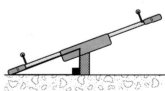

8 A children's climbing frame is 10·8 m long. It meets
the ground at an angle of 38°. How high is its vertical
support?

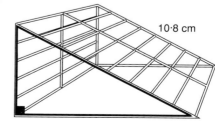

10·8 cm

Bearing up

● **Remember**

Three figure bearings are measured clockwise from North.

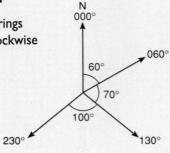

1 Write the three figure bearing of each town.

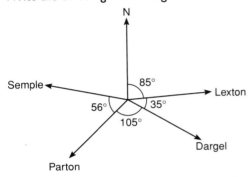

A ship sails 59 km from Buckie on a bearing of 072°. It then turns onto a bearing of 270° and sails until it is due north of Buckie. How far is it from Buckie?

Sketch its route, marking angles and distances.

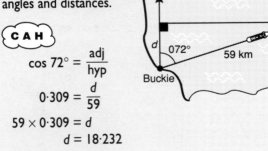

CAH

$$\cos 72° = \frac{adj}{hyp}$$

$$0.309 = \frac{d}{59}$$

$$59 \times 0.309 = d$$

$$d = 18.232$$

The ship is **18 km** from Buckie.

2 A ship sails 32 km from port on a bearing of 048°. It turns onto a bearing of 180° and sails until it is due east of its starting point.

(a) Sketch the ship's route, marking all angle sizes and distances.

(b) How far is the ship from port?

3 An aircraft flies on a bearing of 220° for 178 km. It then flies on a bearing of 090° until it is due south of its starting point.

(a) Sketch the route of the aircraft.

(b) How far is the aircraft from its starting point?

4 The diagram shows the course of a yacht race.

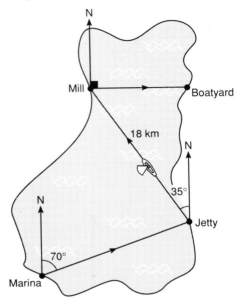

(a) Find the bearing:
   • from the marina to the jetty
   • from the jetty to the mill
   • from the mill to the boatyard.

(b) The boatyard is due north of the jetty. Sketch the triangle joining the jetty, the mill and the boatyard, marking in angles and distances.

(c) Find the distance from the mill to the boatyard.

▼ **Challenge**

5 A flight navigator has plotted her route on a map. Use her diagram to calculate the bearing from Gorton to Fritzburg.

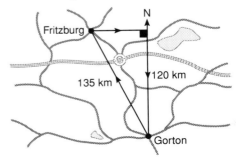

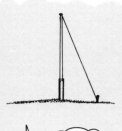

This flagpole is 3·82 m high. The guy rope is anchored at an angle of 70° to the ground. How long is the guy rope?

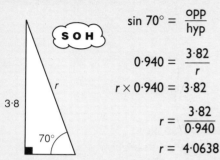

$$\sin 70° = \frac{\text{opp}}{\text{hyp}}$$

$$0.940 = \frac{3.82}{r}$$

$$r \times 0.940 = 3.82$$

$$r = \frac{3.82}{0.940}$$

$$r = 4.0638$$

The rope is 4·06 m, to the nearest cm.

1 Find the length of each guy rope.

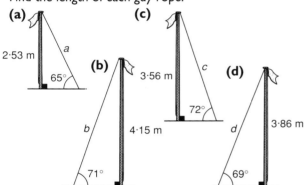

(a) 2·53 m *a* 65°

(b) *b* 71°

(c) 3·56 m *c* 72° 4·15 m

(d) *d* 69° 3·86 m

A support wire from the telegraph pole is anchored to the ground 2·95 m from the pole. The rope makes an angle of 68° with the ground. How long is the wire?

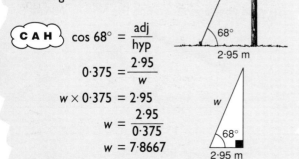

CAH $\cos 68° = \frac{\text{adj}}{\text{hyp}}$

$$0.375 = \frac{2.95}{w}$$

$$w \times 0.375 = 2.95$$

$$w = \frac{2.95}{0.375}$$

$$w = 7.8667$$

The wire is 7·81 m, to the nearest cm.

2 Find the length of each wire.

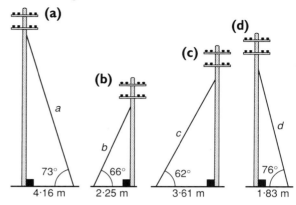

(a) *a* 73° 4·16 m

(b) *b* 66° 2·25 m

(c) *c* 62° 3·61 m

(d) *d* 76° 1·83 m

The tent pole is 1·53 m high. The guy rope is pegged at an angle of 69° to the ground. How far is the peg from the pole?

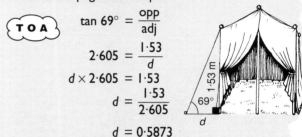

TOA $\tan 69° = \frac{\text{opp}}{\text{adj}}$

$$2.605 = \frac{1.53}{d}$$

$$d \times 2.605 = 1.53$$

$$d = \frac{1.53}{2.605}$$

$$d = 0.5873$$

The peg is 0·59 m from the pole, to the nearest cm.

3 For each ten pole find the distance between the pole and the peg.

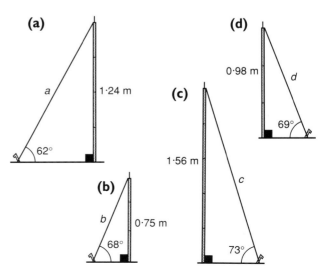

(a) *a* 62° 1·24 m

(b) *b* 68° 0·75 m

(c) 1·56 m *c* 73°

(d) 0·98 m *d* 69°

Find the distance

● **Remember**

SOH CAH TOA

$$\sin = \frac{\text{opp}}{\text{hyp}} \qquad \cos = \frac{\text{adj}}{\text{hyp}} \qquad \tan = \frac{\text{opp}}{\text{adj}}$$

1 Calculate the value of x in each triangle.

(a)

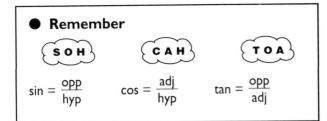

x, 33°, 51 cm

(b)

8 cm, 42°, x

(c)

9 mm, x, 72°

(d)

8·1 m, 62°, x

(e)

15 mm, x, 51°

(f)

x, 18°, 4·3 m

2 A ladder is resting against the top of a wall 1·85 m high. The angle between the ladder and the ground is 63°.

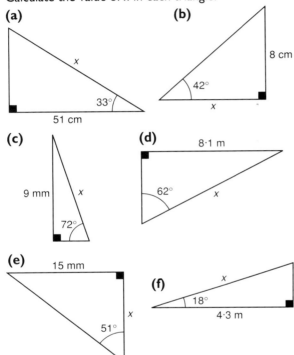

   (a) Sketch the right-angled triangle formed by the ladder, the wall and the ground.

   (b) Calculate the length of the ladder.

3 A ramp has been constructed to a height of 60 cm. The angle between the ramp and the ground is 35°.

Find the length of the base of the ramp.

4 A hole is drilled through a wall at an angle of 42° to the horizontal. How long is the hole?

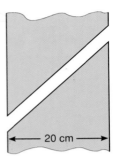

20 cm

5 A fence post is 92 cm high. Calculate the length of its shadow when the sun's rays are at an angle of 56° to the ground.

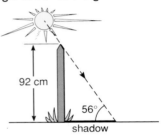

92 cm, 56°, shadow

6 The height of this square pyramid is 22 cm. Each sloping edge is at an angle of 66° to the horizontal. Find s.

22 cm, s, 66°

7 Tommy has drawn this plan of a roof structure. Beam A is in the centre of the structure.

   (a) Find the length of beam A.

   (b) Use your answer to find the length of beam B.

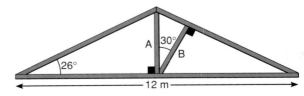

A, 30°, B, 26°, 12 m

1 Calculate the value of *x* in each triangle.

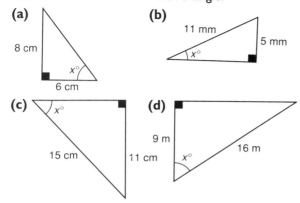

(a)
8 cm
6 cm
x°

(b)
11 mm
5 mm
x°

(c)
x°
15 cm

(d)
9 m
11 cm
16 m
x°

2 Calculate *d* in each triangle.

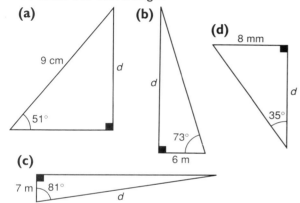

(a)
9 cm
d
51°

(b)
d
73°
6 m

(d)
8 mm
d
35°

(c)
7 m
81°
d

3 For this wall bracket find the length, *l*.

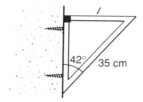

l
42°
35 cm

4 Calculate the angle between the rafter and the wall.

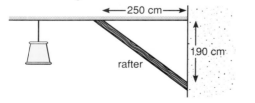

←250 cm→
190 cm
rafter

5 Calculate the length of the longest side of the set square.

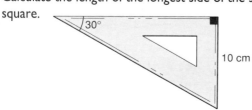

30°
10 cm

6 A rescue helicopter is hovering at a height of 300 m above the buoy. It is observed from two yachts, P and Q. The angle of elevation of the helicopter is 45° from P and 63° from Q.

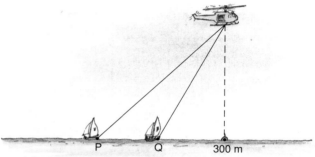

P   Q   300 m

(a) Calculate the distance from Q to the buoy.

(b) Find the distance between P and Q.

7 For this plan of a barn loft:

(a) calculate length *d*

(b) find angle *x*.

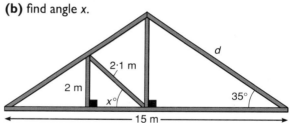

d
2·1 m
2 m
x°
35°
←————— 15 m —————→

8 From Port Amity a cruiser sailed due south for 25 km. It then altered course onto a bearing of 060° and sailed until it was due east of the port.

(a) Sketch the course of the cruiser.

(b) How far is the cruiser from Port Amity?

(c) Calculate the distance sailed on the second leg of the journey.

Brian works for Swift Mail Order Company. He consults graphs to find the delivery charge for different goods.

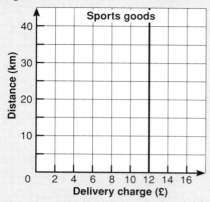

This graph for sports goods shows that the delivery charge is £12 and does not depend on the distance the goods are being sent.

1 In the same way draw separate graphs to show delivery charges for each item.

Item	Furniture	Clothes	Toys
Cost for all distances	£16	£10	£7

2 (a) Write the coordinates of the points A, B, C and D shown on this straight line graph.

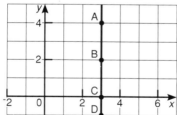

(b) What do you notice about the x-coordinates?

The x-coordinate of all points on the line above is 3. This means that the equation of the line is x = 3

3 (a) List 4 points with x-coordinate 7.
(b) Draw the graph of x = 7.

4 On the same coordinate diagram draw the graphs of:
(a) x = 1   (b) x = 4   (c) x = 9
(d) x = ⁻3   (e) x = ⁻5   (f) x = 0

Brian also consults this graph.

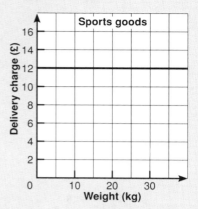

This graph for sports goods shows that the delivery charge is £12 and does not depend on the weight of the goods.

5 In the same way draw separate graphs to show delivery charges for each item.

Item	Furniture	Clothes	Toys
Cost for all weights	£16	£10	£7

6 (a) Write the coordinates of the points A, B, C and D shown on this straight line graph.

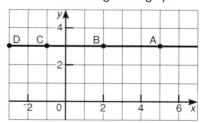

(b) What do you notice about the y-coordinates?

The y-coordinate of all points on the line above is 3. The equation of the line is y = 3

7 (a) List 4 points with y-coordinate 8.
(b) Draw the graph of y = 8.

8 On the same coordinate diagram draw the graphs of:
(a) y = 2   (b) y = 10   (c) y = 5
(d) y = ⁻4   (e) y = ⁻7   (f) y = 0

Graphical inequations:
$x \geqslant c, x \leqslant c, y \geqslant c, y \leqslant c$
$y \geqslant c, y \leqslant c$

124

Annette works for Rapide Mail Order Co.
She consults this graph for delivery charges.

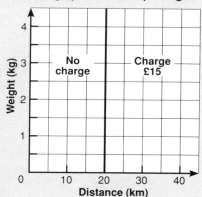

9 (a) Copy and complete this table of delivery charges.

Weight	4 kg	2·5 kg	3 kg	1·5 kg
Distance	10 km	30 km	5 km	12 km
Delivery charge				

(b) What is the delivery charge for any distance less than 20 km?

(c) What is the delivery charge for any distance of 20 km or more?

10 The straight line on this graph has equation $x = 5$. The line splits the graph into two regions.

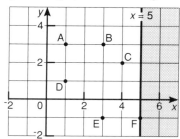

(a) Write the coordinates of the points A to F.
(b) Write the maximum value of the x-coordinate of any point in the unshaded region, including the line $x = 5$

The line above has equation $x = 5$
The **unshaded area** represents the inequation $x \leqslant 5$

11 On separate coordinate diagrams show unshaded regions to represent:
(a) $x \leqslant 2$ (b) $x \geqslant 7$ (c) $x \leqslant {}^-1$ (d) $x \geqslant 1$

12 The straight line on this graph has equation $y = 3$. The line splits the graph into two regions.

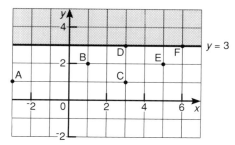

(a) Write the coordinates of the points A to F.
(b) Write the maximum value of the y-coordinate of any point in the unshaded region, including the line $y = 3$.

The line above has equation $y = 3$.
The **unshaded** area represents the inequation $y \leqslant 3$

13 On separate coordinate diagrams show unshaded regions to represent:
(a) $y \leqslant 4$ (b) $y \geqslant 1$ (c) $y \leqslant {}^-2$ (d) $y \geqslant 5$

14 For each graph write the inequation representing the unshaded region.

(a)

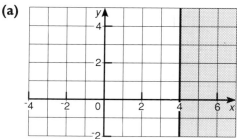

(b)

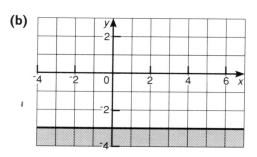

No extra charge

Shamiana works for Transit Carriers.
She uses a formula to work out delivery charges.
For a distance(d) in km and a weight (w) in kg:

If *distance* + 2 × *weight* < 10 then no charge.
If *distance* + 2 × *weight* ≥ 10 then charge £15.

If $d + 2w < 10$ then no charge
If $d + 2w \geqslant 10$ then charge £15

BLUE STAR CARRIERS

You need a blue and a red pencil.

1 **(a)** Copy and complete the table.

Distance (d)	Weight (w)	d + 2w	Charge £
1	4	9	0
3	3		
4	4		
6	6		
4	3		
5	1		
3	2		
6	2		

(b) Copy the graph. Using the table, mark in blue the points representing no charge.

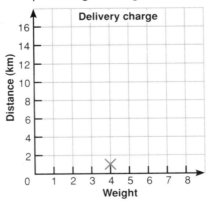

Delivery charge

(c) Using the table, mark in red the points representing a £15 charge.
(d) Mark in blue other points representing no charge.
(e) Mark in red other points representing a charge of £15.
(f) Draw the line representing $d + 2w = 10$.

2 Kirsten works for Blue Star Carriers.
She uses this formula to work out delivery charges.
If *distance* + 4 × *weight* < 12 then no charge.
If *distance* + 4 × *weight* ≥ 12 then charge £15.

If $d + 4w < 12$ then no charge
If $d + 4w \geqslant 12$ then charge £15

(a) Copy and complete the table.

Distance (d)	Weight (w)	d + 4w	Charge £
1	1	5	0
2	3		
1	2		
6	1		
3	3		
7	1		
5	2		

(b) On a graph, mark in blue the points from the table representing no charge.
(c) Using the table, mark in red the points representing a £15 charge.
(d) Mark in blue other points representing no charge.
(e) Mark in red other points representing a charge of £15.
(f) Draw the line representing $d + 4w = 12$.

Graphcal
inequations:
$ax + by \leqslant c$
$ax + by \geqslant c$

126

This graph shows distances and weights for which Blue Star Carriers make no delivery charge.

The **unshaded region** represents the points where $d + 4w < 12$
where d is the distance in km and
  w is the weight in kg.

The line $d + 4w = 12$ is a boundary of the region. It is a **dashed line** to show that points on the line **are not included** in the region.

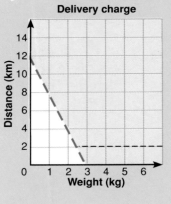

Delivery charge

This graph shows distances and weights for which Blue Star Carriers makes a charge of £12.
The **unshaded region** represents the points where $d + 4w \geqslant 12$.
The line $d + 4w = 12$ is a boundary of the region. It is a **solid line** to show that points on the line **are included** in the region.

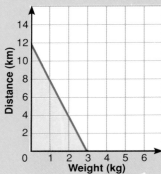

3 Same Day Deliveries use graphs of these inequations to decide on their charges.
$d + 3w < 9$ No charge
$d + 3w \geqslant 9$ £15 charge
Show each on a separate diagram.

4 For each of the following:
  • draw a graph representing the equation
  • show the region representing the inequation.
  (a) $d + 2w = 4$ and $d + 2w \leqslant 4$
  (b) $d + 2w = 4$ and $d + 2w \geqslant 4$
  (c) $d + w = 10$ and $d + w \leqslant 10$
  (d) $d + w = 10$ and $d + w \geqslant 10$

If the inequation is < or > use a dashed line.
If the inequation is ⩽ or ⩾ use a solid line.

5 Show on a graph the regions where:
  (a) $y + x < 8$ **(b)** $y + 2x < 10$
  (c) $y + 4x > 16$ **(d)** $2y + x \geqslant 8$
  (e) $3y + 2x \leqslant 12$ **(f)** $2y + 3x < 6$

▼ Challenge

6 This diagram shows the regions where both Transit and Blue Star make a £15 charge.

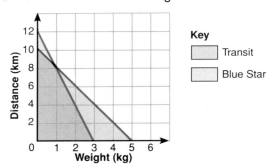

Key
  ▢ Transit
  ▢ Blue Star

(a) For each of the following, state which company you would use. In each case give a reason.
  • distance 5 km, weight 2 kg
  • distance 1 km, weight 3 kg
  • distance 11 km, weight 0·1 kg
  • distance 3 km, weight 4 kg

(b) Stephan runs *Copyright Press*. He has goods of different weights delivered to his customers throughout his local area. Advise him as to which company to use.

1 The fishing boat *Harvester* is 25 km south west of Aberdruie harbour.

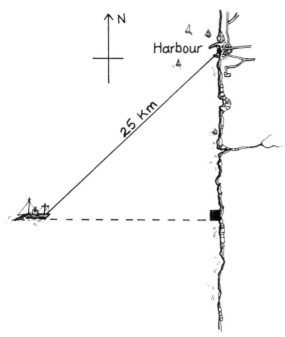

(a) Calculate how far the boat is from the nearest land.

(b) *Harvester* sets sail for the harbour on a bearing of 050°. If the skipper does not alter course, calculate how far the boat will be from the harbour when it runs aground.

2 In his will John Doe left a sum of £22 750 to his sons William and Alex.

(a) William received £8500 more than Alex. How much did each brother receive?

(b) If Mr Doe had split his money in the ratio 3:2 how much would each brother have received?

3 Which would you rather have, a present of £2^5 or a present of £5^2? Explain.

4 A group of students is going to the swimming pool. Seven of the group walk and the rest travel by mini-bus. The bus has to make three trips, fully loaded each time.
On the way back, eighteen students walk and the mini-bus makes only two trips, fully loaded.

(a) How many students does the mini-bus hold?

(b) How many students are there in the group?

5

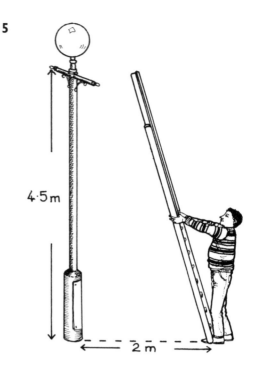

Jim has to repair this street light.
The ladder-rest on the lamppost is 4·5 m from the ground and the ladder will extend to 5 m. Jim puts the foot of the ladder 2 m from the lamppost.

(a) Will the ladder reach the rest? Explain.

(b) What angle does the ladder make with the ground?

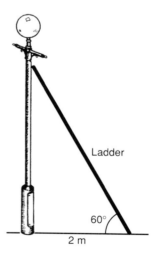

(c) Jim has to fix an identification plate to the lamppost. He shortens the ladder and rests it against the lamppost, making an angle of 60° with the ground.
Calculate the length of the ladder now.

6

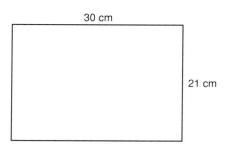

30 cm

21 cm

Indu needs a circular piece of card with an area of
340 cm. Can she cut one from this rectangle?

7 For any graph of speed against time, the **area under
the graph** gives the total distance travelled.

(a) This graph shows the flight of a Jumbo jet from
Shannon to the eastern United States.

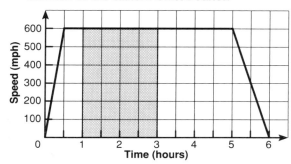

How far did the plane fly during the second two
hours of its flight?

(b) This graph shows the crossing of a car ferry
from St Malo to Portsmouth.

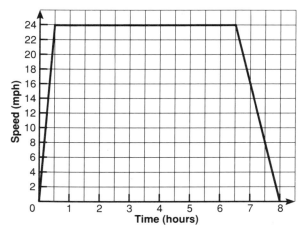

Find the total distance sailed by the ferry.

8 The average weight of the Academicals 1st XV
rugby team is 96 kg. The weight of the scrum half is
82 kg. Find the average weight of the other 14
players.

9 Mr Fazzinni sells coffee
beans in his delicatessen.
He makes his *Special Blend* by
mixing Kenyan beans with
Brazilian beans in the
ratio 4 : 7

Mr Fazzinni has 20 kg of Kenyan beans and 28 kg of
Brazilian beans in stock. What is the maximum
weight of *Special Blend* he can mix?

10 J. Carrot is a jeweller. One of his necklace designs is
made by joining small rings with strands of fine
chain.

(a) Copy and complete the table.

Number of rings (R)	1	2	3	4	5	6
Number of strands (S)	0	5				

(b) How many strands of chain would J. Carrot use
for 8 rings?

(c) Find a formula connecting S and R.

(d) How many strands of chain would he use for
17 rings?

(e) J. Carrot used 125 strands of chain for his Grand
Duchess necklace. How many rings are in this
necklace?

1 This is a plan of two flower beds in Jubilee Park.

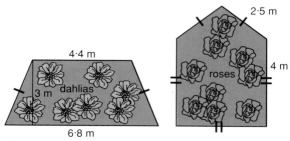

Find:

(a) the area of the dahlia bed

(b) the perimeter of the rose bed.

2 Frank has 9 metres of guttering. Does he have enough to replace the guttering on the two edges of this outbuilding?

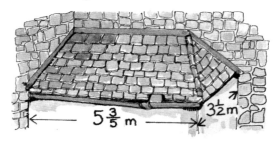

3 (a) Calculate the volume of water in Alison's fish tank.

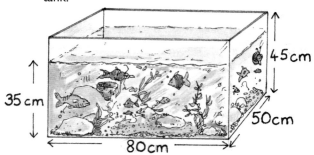

(b) Can 50 litres of water be added to the tank?

4 In 1980, the population of Baldoile was 12 560. Four years later the population had risen by 5%. What was the population in 1984?

5 Multiply out:

(a) $4(x + 3)$ **(b)** $3(2a - 5)$

6 Simplify:

(a) $5p + 7q + p - 2q$ **(b)** $2(4x - 3) + 5x$

7 120 students identified their favourite subject. The pie chart shows the results.

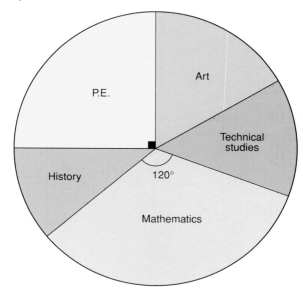

How many students chose:

(a) Mathematics

(b) PE?

8 Michelle works for RadioPhonics. She uses this formula to calculate customers' bills:
$$C = 1.2 (12h + p)$$
where C is the total cost cost in pounds

     n is the number of hours spent on the repair and

     p is the cost of the parts in pounds.

Find the total cost of repairing a video recorder which required parts worth £23 and took 2 hours to repair.

9 The school roll of Wellwood High School is 1060. Three fifths of the school's students travel to school by bus. How many students is this?

10 Solve:

(a) $7h + 11 = 5h + 25$

(b) $7x < 20 - 3x$

(c) $10(7m - 6) = 150$

1 Harriet can lay 36 bricks every 12 minutes.

(a) How many bricks can she lay in:
  • 16 minutes • $\frac{1}{2}$ an hour?
(b) How long should it take her to lay:
  • 54 bricks • 198 bricks?

2 The scale of this map is 1 : 250 000

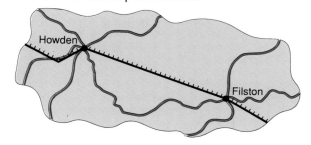

What is the true length, in kilometres, of the canal between Howden and Filston?

3 A lifeboat leaves Port Harburn on a bearing of 130°. It sails 80 kilometres to a fishing boat where it picks up an injured fisherman. It then sails 50 km to Beachy Point on a bearing of 065°.

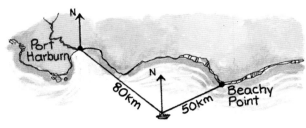

(a) Using a suitable scale, make a scale drawing of the lifeboat's route.
(b) Use your scale drawing to find:
  • the distance from Beachy Point to Port Harburn
  • the bearing of Port Harburn from Beachy Point.

4 Five days have been allocated for 30 volunteers to clean a stretch of canal. Only 25 volunteers turn up. How much longer should be allowed?

5 Stacks of barrels are arranged in three layers. Here are the first three stacks in the pattern.

(a) Draw the next stack in the pattern.
(b) Copy and complete.

Stack number (s)	1	2	3	4	5
Number of barrels (b)					

(c) Write a formula for the number of barrels.
(d) Use your formula to find the number of barrels in Stack 10.

6 Find the values of a to f in this kite.

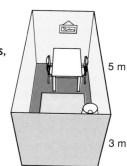

7 Round:
(a) 2·4536 to 2 decimal places
(b) 10·765 to 3 significant figures
(c) 7246 to 1 significant figure.

8 Write the lower and upper bounds of these measurements.
(a) (15 ± 0.2) mm
(b) (0.055 ± 0.0005) cm

9 Decorators can use this formula to estimate the number of rolls of wallpaper needed to decorate a room.

$$N = \frac{H \times P}{5}$$

where N is the number of rolls,
  H is the height of the room in metres and
  P is the perimeter of the room in metres.
How many rolls of wallpaper would a decorator need to buy to decorate this room?

1 Find:

(a) $5 - 8$ (b) $^-7 - 3$ (c) $4 + ^-8$

(d) $4 \times ^-7$ (e) $^-36 \div 9$ (f) $7 - ^-9$

(g) $3 - ^-2 + 8$ (h) $\dfrac{5 \times ^-6}{^-10}$

2 Simplify:

(a) $3(3x - 2)$ (b) $6x - (x + 2)$

(c) $4(3y - 1) + 2(y + 4)$ (d) $9y - 5(2y - 3)$

3 Solve:

(a) $5p = 3p - 16$ (b) $18 - 9m = 54$

(c) $\dfrac{8r}{^-2} = ^-12$ (d) $^-4(2a + 7) = 68$

4 Douglas picks a marble at random from a bag containing 6 blue, 8 red and 4 yellow marbles. Find:

(a) P(blue)   (b) P(red)

(c) P(not yellow)

5 The table shows one week's sales of crisps at the school tuck shop.

Cheese	Tomato	Vinegar	Garlic	Plain
80	75	106	32	57

(a) For this week what is the relative frequency of:
• tomato   • garlic?

(b) The following week, total sales of 280 packets are expected. How many packets of tomato crisps do you think will be sold?

6 Find the difference between the cash price and the HP price.

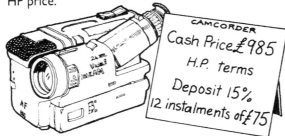

CAMCORDER

Cash Price £985

H.P. terms

Deposit 15%

12 instalments of £75

7 Carrick borrowed £1250 over 6 months at 16% pa to replace a fireplace.

(a) Calculate the interest he has to pay.

(b) How much is each monthly repayment?

8 Ka Man lives in Area B and insures her house for £113 000.
Calculate her premium.

Smartsure Insurance	
Area	Premium per £100 of sum insured
A	19p
B	25p
C	31p

9 Susan rents a car for a fixed charge of £12 plus £16 per day.

(a) Copy and complete the table.

Number of days	Cost (£)
1	28
2	
3	
4	

(b) Find a formula for the cost.

(c) Use your formula to find the cost to Susan of renting a car for 18 days.

10 'A cyclist pedalled at a steady speed, stopped for a short break, cycled up a steep hill and freewheeled down the other side.'
Which distance/time graph fits this description?

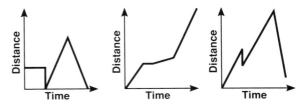

11 A bicycle wheel has a diameter of 24 inches.

(a) Calculate the circumference of the wheel.

(b) How far would the bicycle travel in 25 revolutions of the wheel?

(c) How many metres is this if there are approximately 39 inches in a metre?

12 Calculate the area of this patio to one decimal place.

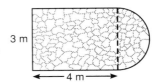

3 m

4 m

1 The table shows the costs for one adult for three hotels in Corsica.

Date of departure	*No. of nights*	Hotel *Paoli*	*Rena*	*Cinarca*
1–31 May	7 14	339 479	359 479	479 559
1–30 June	7 14	405 545	465 575	608 695
1–31 July	7 14	439 689	479 739	655 735
Children aged 2–12, 40% reduction				

Find the cost of a two week holiday at the Hotel Rena for three adults and an eight-year-old child, leaving on 14 June.

2 When Tom was in Corsica the exchange rate was 8·19 French francs to the £. If the bank charged him 2% commission, how many francs did he receive for £230?

3 The distance from Calvi to Ajaccio is 75 km. How long would this journey take in a car travelling at an average speed of 60 km/h?

4 The scale factor, k, is given for each pair of similar shapes. Find the length of the named side.

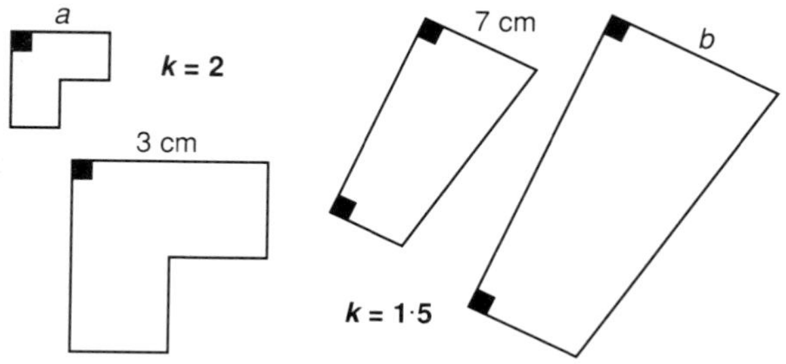

5 Find PR.

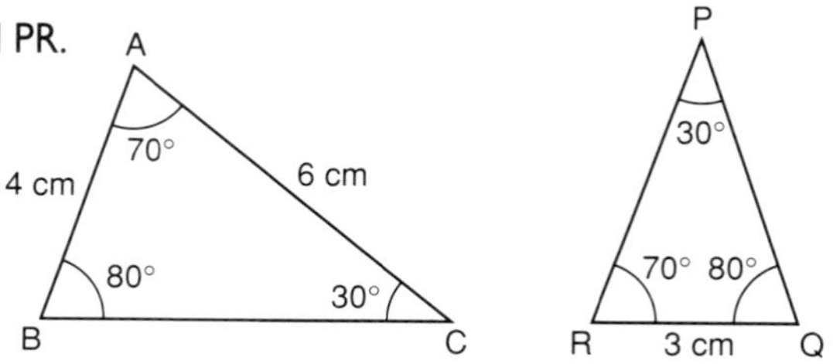

6 The area of a pattern piece is 130 cm^2. An enlargement is made using scale factor 3. What is the area of the enlarged piece?

7 During a two week period Mrs Seagrave recorded the number of daily absences for Year 11.

12 8 6 7 6
9 10 11 5 6

Find the mean, median and mode of these absences.

8 At Barnside Primary School Class 3 drew a graph of the house points they gained.

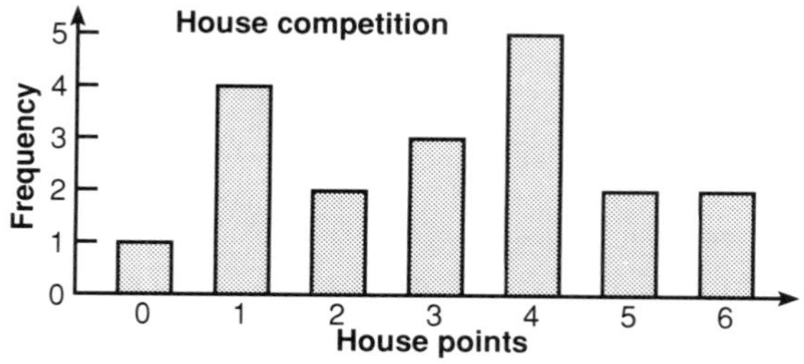

Find the mean, median and mode.

9 This frequency table shows the marks gained by students in year 11 in an English test.

Test mark	*Frequency*
1–5	2
6–10	12
11–15	21
16–20	10

Calculate the mean mark.

10 Calculate the value of x to 1 dp in each triangle.

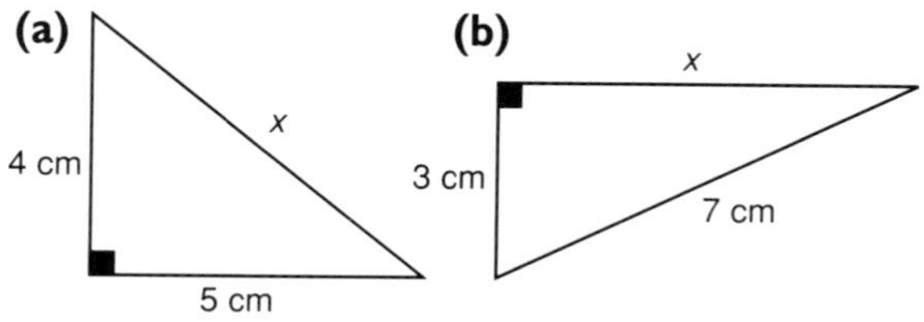

11 Find the height of the tent pole.

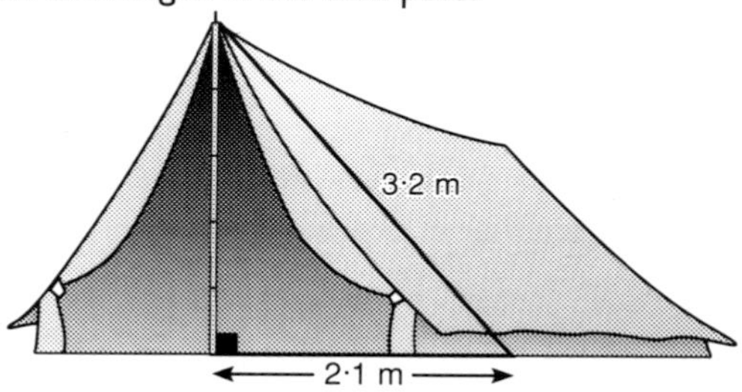

12 Calculate the distance between points A(1, 3) and B(7, 11).

1 Simplify:
 (a) $7x + 5x$ (b) $8w + 6v - 2w + 3v$

2 Multiply:
 (a) $3(2x + 4y)$ (b) $5(4b - 7c)$

3 Simplify:
 (a) $4(3x + 5y) + 6x$ (b) $6(2f + 8g) + 2(4f - 9g)$

4 Factorise:
 (a) $8x + 6$ (b) $9v - 12h + 6k$ (c) $a^2 + 5a$
 (d) $4f^2 + 4gf - f$ (e) $4t^2 + 12st$

5 Multiply these brackets.
 (a) $(x + 3)(x + 2)$ (b) $(y + 4)(y - 3)$
 (c) $(f - 5)(f - 7)$ (d) $(p - 2)(p + 1)$

6 Calculate:
 (a) $\frac{2}{3}$ of $\frac{3}{4}$ (b) $\frac{3}{7} \times \frac{7}{8}$ (c) $\frac{2}{5} \times \frac{2}{3}$

7 In Class 5B, $\frac{3}{4}$ of the students have blue eyes. Of these, $\frac{3}{5}$ wear glasses. What fraction of the class wear glasses and have blue eyes?

8 Calculate:
 (a) $\frac{2}{3} \div \frac{2}{5}$ (b) $\frac{5}{8} \div \frac{3}{4}$ (c) $\frac{3}{10} \div \frac{2}{3}$

9 How many glasses each containing $\frac{2}{5}$ of a pint can be filled from a barrel containing 4 pints?

10 Orange squash and water are mixed in the ratio $3 : 7$ to make a drink. How much water is needed when the amount of orange squash is:
 (a) 12 ml (b) 15 ml (c) 36 ml?

11 In a golf club the ratio of women to men is $3 : 5$. How many members are women, if the total membership is 312?

12 The roof space of Jack's house forms a triangular prism.

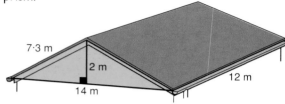

 (a) Calculate the volume of the roof space.
 (b) Jack wants to line the underside of the sloping roof and the floor of the roof space with insulation. What is the total area of insulation which he should order?

13 (a) Calculate the volume of this pipe.
 (Volume of cylinder = $\pi r^2 h$)

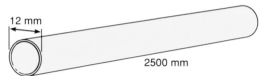

 (b) Calculate the surface area of this pipe.

14 Gemma and her friends are playing a game with a red and a blue die.

Find:
 (a) P(blue die score shows an even number)
 (b) P(total is 3)
 (c) P(2 fours)
 (d) P(total is greater than 10)
 (e) P(blue die shows 5 and red die shows 3)
 (f) P(blue die shows 5 or red die shows 3)

15 Isaac is a joiner and is paid an hourly rate of £5·25 for a basic 35 hour week. Overtime is paid at time and a half. Calculate his gross wage for a week in which he worked for 40 hours.

16 Roberta sells kitchens and earns $7\frac{1}{2}\%$ commission on all her sales. Find her commission if her sales total was £12 650.

1 Calculate the average speed for each journey in Cassie's log book.

2 Rowan cycled for 1 h 45 mins at an average speed of 24 km/h. How far did she cycle?

3 The graph shows Chris's journey by bus and train from Eaglesham to Ayr via Glasgow.

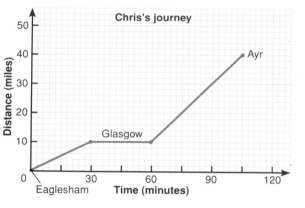

(a) How long did Chris spend in Glasgow?
(b) How far is it from Glasgow to Ayr?
(c) What was the average speed of the train?

4 Find the value of x to 1 decimal place in each triangle.

(a)

(b)

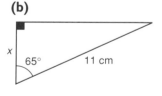

5 Vicky is playing on an aerial runway. Calculate the angle between the wire and the ground.

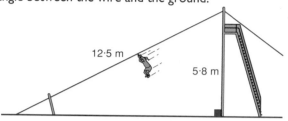

6 For each set of data find:
 • the median
 • the upper and lower quartiles
 • the inter-quartile range.
 (a) 5, 1, 4, 4, 8, 7, 9, 3, 14, 6, 2
 (b) 13, 5, 26, 12, 5, 8, 12, 23, 19
 (c) 21, 33, 20, 38, 29, 29, 30, 35

7 Roisin is making matchstick patterns.

Pattern number

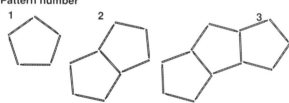

(a) Copy and complete Roisin's table.

Pattern number (p)	1	2	3	4	5
Number of matchsticks (m)	5	9			

(b) Copy and complete her formula.

$m = \boxed{} \, p + \boxed{}$

(c) What type of graph would you expect from this formula?
(d) Draw the graph.

8 Find the coordinates of each point on the graph of $y = x^2 + 3$ when the x coordinate is:
 (a) 4   (b) 0   (c) 5   (d) ⁻3

1 Phil is trying to find the weight of a box of chocolates. The boxes on the scales are identical. Form an equation and solve it to find the weight of one box.

2 Solve:
   (a) $7x + 6 = 41$
   (b) $19 - 5c = 2c + 5$
   (c) $5p - 6 < 24$
   (d) $17 + 6d > 13d - 4$
   (e) $5(4y + 3) = 35$
   (f) $18 = 3(5x - 4)$
   (g) $\frac{7t}{3} = 7$
   (h) $\frac{4p}{5} - 3 = 17$

3 Mack Ltd use this formula to calculate the starting salary for their employees:
   $$S = 6000 + 50Y$$
   where S is the starting salary in £ and
   Y is the age in years.
   (a) Find the starting salary for Frank, aged 22.
   (b) Make Y the subject of the formula.
   (c) Mary's starting salary is £7200. How old is she?

4 Seventy square metres of carpet are needed to cover this floor. Find the length l metres.

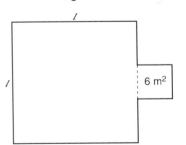

5 Find the gradient of this wedge.

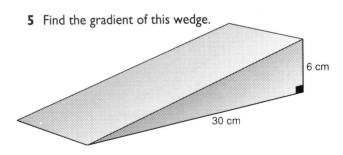

6 Grace is a blacksmith. She uses this table to find how much to charge her customers.

Time in hours (h)	1	2	3	4
Charge in £(c)	12	21	30	39

Draw a graph and find the equation of the line.

7 The kinetic energy of a moving body is found from the formula $E = \frac{1}{2} mv^2$
   where E is the kinetic energy in Joules,
   m is the mass in kilograms and
   v is the velocity in metres per second.
   Find the kinetic energy of a stone of mass 0·6 kg travelling with a velocity of 4 m/s.

8 In 1982 the population of the United Kingdom was 54 800 000. Express this population in standard form.

9 A nanometre is a distance of 0·000 000 001 metres. Express this distance in scientific notation.

10 The speed of light is $3·0 \times 10^8$ m/s. How far will light travel in 1 minute?

11 Robbie is rowing a boat directly across a stream, 100 metres wide. He starts at a point directly opposite a jetty. For every 10 metres Robbie rows across the stream, the current pushes him 2 metres downstream to his right.

Make a scale drawing and mark Robbie's position for every 10 metres that he rows.
How far downstream will he land?

1 In exchanging money, the number of francs, *F*, varies directly as the number of pounds, *P*.

Jenny exchanged 675 francs for £75.

(a) Find the constant of variation.

(b) Write the formula connecting *F* and *P*.

(c) How many francs would Jenny get for £110?

2 (a) Sarah has completed a table of speed against time for her journey home from school.

Time in minutes (t)	10	20	30	40
Speed in mph (s)	24	12	8	6

Draw a graph of *s* against *t*.
Does *s* vary directly as *t*? Explain.

(b) Copy and complete this table.

$\frac{1}{t}$	0·1	0·05		
s	24	12	8	6

(c) Draw a graph of *s* against $\frac{1}{t}$.

(d) Find the constant of variation.

(e) Find *t* when *s* is: • 16 mph • 10 mph.

3 Solve each pair of simultaneous equations.

(a) $x + y = 6$
$x + 3y = 10$

(b) $4x + y = 14$
$3x - y = 0$

4 One pen and two rulers cost £1·09.
Two pens and one ruler cost £1·22.
Find the price of a pen.

5 Write the value of:

(a) 5^3 (b) 2^5 (c) 10^7 (d) 8^4

(e) $1^{\frac{1}{4}}$ (f) $16^{\frac{1}{2}}$ (g) $\sqrt[3]{0}$ (h) $\sqrt[4]{81}$

6 Simplify:

(a) $5^3 \times 5^7$ (b) $p^2 \times p^3$
(c) $2a^3 \times 4a^5$ (d) $7^{11} \div 7^5$
(e) $r^{12} \div r^2$ (f) $48c^5 \div 12c^2$
(g) $(4r)^3$ (h) $(10s)^5$

7 (a) List four points with *x*-coordinate 5.
(b) Draw the graph of *x* = 5.
(c) Show the unshaded region representing *x* ⩾ 5.

8 On a coordinate diagram show the unshaded region representing *y* + 2*x* < 8.

9 A yacht sails 7 km from harbour on a bearing of 078°. It then turns and sails due south. Calculate the minimum distance between the yacht and the harbour on this leg of the journey.

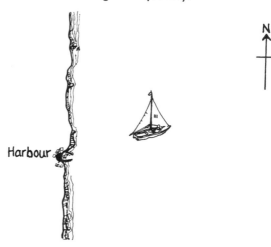

10 In each diagram calculate the value of *x*, to 1 decimal place.

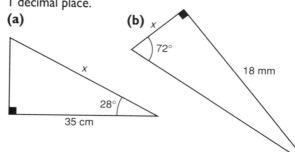

(a)

x

28°

35 cm

(b) *x*

72°

18 mm

Answers for textbook

Page 1   Camilla's Candies

1. (a) $(16t + 8f + 20c)$ pence
   (b) $(18t + 9f + 24c)$ pence
   (c) $(38t + 19f + 50c)$ pence
   (d) $(64t + 32f + 83c)$ pence
2. (a) $7x$ (b) $3m$ (c) $8y$ (d) $11s$ (e) $10r$
   (f) d (g) $9a + 9b$ (h) $2p + 15q$ (i) $w + 7z$
   (j) $2m + n$ (k) $11r + 3s + 16t$
   (l) $13a + 2b - 16c$ (m) $2v + 20$
   (n) $10g - 5$ (o) $5k + 2j + 5$
3. (a) $12x + 8y$ (b) $15a + 5b$
   (c) $28m - 35n$ (d) $21g - 12h$
   (e) $10f + 30g$ (f) $4s - 12t$
   (g) $66f + 33g + 22$ (h) $32a - 48b + 56$
   (i) $8x - 40y - 32$ (j) $15r + 21s + 9$
4. (a) $16x + 25y$ (b) $26g + 26f$
   (c) $38r + 16s$ (d) $42m - 52n$
   (e) $48c + 15$ (f) $77h + 49$
   (g) $17a + 27b + 2c$ (h) $51p - 12q$
   (i) $10a + 35b + 40d$ (j) $36d + 30e + 48$
   (k) $51r + 28s + 23t$ (l) $53a + 19b - 27$

Page 2   Finding factors

1. (a) $7(m + n)$ (b) $8(f - g)$ (c) $4(c + d)$ (d) $6(r + s)$
   (e) $4(t - 3)$ (f) $6(m + 4)$
2. (a) $2(2m + 3n)$ (b) $7(2r + 3s)$ (c) $5(2p - 5q)$
   (d) $3(j - 3k)$ (e) $3(2t + 5)$ (f) $7(a + 7)$
   (g) $8(2h + 3j)$ (h) $20(x - 5)$ (i) $9(2w - 9z)$
   (j) $2(6a + 2b + 5c)$ (k) $7(2m - 4n + 5)$ (l) $6(6p - 10q - 1)$
   (m) $3(5f + 11g - 9h)$ (n) $11(2x - 5y + 11)$ (o) $4(8d - 4e + 1)$
3. (a) $m(m + 6)$ (b) $t(t + 7)$
   (c) $r(r - 3)$ (d) $s(5 + t)$
   (e) $g(3 - f)$ (f) $d(e + g)$
   (g) $b(3b + 5)$ (h) $m(7m - 6n)$
   (i) $w(2w - 7z)$ (j) $f(f + 3g - 6)$
   (k) $r(r - 2s - 5t)$ (l) $m(m - 5n + 8p)$
   (m) $x(x + 9y - 9)$ (n) $d(5c + 4e + 7f)$
   (o) $h(3h - 8g - 9)$ (p) $s(3t - 5t + 7)$
   (q) $a(2a + 4bc - c)$ (r) $w(3w - 6x + 7xy)$
   (s) $x(8z + 8y - 1)$
4. (a) $3x(x + 3y)$ (b) $5y(y - 3z)$ (c) $4r(2r + 3s)$
   (d) $3a(2b + 3c)$ (e) $5m(2n + 5m)$ (f) $7u(v - 3w)$
   (g) $12c(2a - b)$ (h) $5r(3s - 7t)$ (i) $2f(8f + g)$
   (j) $3x(3x - y + 5)$ (k) $2r(6s - 7t - 5w)$ (l) $11f(2g + 3h + 4f)$
   (m) $16j(k + 2mn)$ (n) $6p(5p - 4q + 3r)$ (o) $7b(4ac - 3bd)$
5. (a) $7(p - 2g)$ (b) $4(3m + 2n)$ (c) $5(5r + 3)$
   (d) $5(4a + 3b - c)$ (e) $9(2u - 3v - 4w)$ (f) $2(15p - 6q + 4)$
   (g) $5(9x + 11y + 7)$ (h) $a(a + 3)$ (i) $b(b - 5)$
   (j) $n(n + 3m)$ (k) $p(q + 7r)$ (l) $f(3f - 5g + 6)$
   (m) $3j(d - 2c + 3)$ (n) $2r(s + 2p + 4r)$ (o) $4x(2y + 3w - 4z)$
   (p) $3u(5v - 1 - 3u)$ (q) $10a(2bc + cd - 3bd)$

Page 3   Tease it out

1. (a) 72 (b) 130 (c) 72 (d) 182
2. (a) $x^2 + 7x + 10$ (b) $x^2 + 15x + 56$ (c) $a^2 + 11a + 24$
   (d) $a^2 + 11a + 30$ (e) $p^2 + 19p + 88$ (f) $t^2 + 9t + 8$
   (g) $f^2 + 16f + 48$ (h) $m^2 + 20m + 10$ (i) $s^2 + 14s + 33$
   (j) $v^2 + 20v + 64$
3. (a) $x^2 + 5x - 14$ (b) $x^2 + 3x - 4$ (c) $t^2 + t - 6$
   (d) $p^2 + 2p - 35$ (e) $a^2 - 4a - 45$ (f) $m^2 + 5m - 66$
   (g) $f^2 + 5f - 24$ (h) $g^2 - 6g - 72$ (i) $y^2 + y - 110$
   (j) $x^2 - x - 30$ (k) $r^2 - 25$ (l) $a^2 - 81$
   (m) $b^2 - 9$ (n) $q^2 - 9q - 10$
4. (a) $x^2 - 10x + 24$ (b) $y^2 - 13y + 40$ (c) $p^2 - 7p + 10$
   (d) $t^2 - 17t + 70$ (e) $a^2 - 10a + 25$ (f) $m^2 - 10m + 9$

Page 4   Home World

5. (a) $a^2 + 16a + 55$ (b) $b^2 + 16b + 63$ (c) $m^2 + 12m + 36$
   (d) $p^2 + 12p + 20$ (e) $f^2 + f - 20$ (f) $r^2 + 3r - 28$
   (g) $x^2 - 7x + 12$ (h) $y^2 - 17y + 70$

1. (a) $\frac{4}{5}$ kg   (b) $\frac{2}{5}$ kg
2. (a) $\frac{1}{3}$ (b) $\frac{1}{5}$ (c) $\frac{2}{7}$ (d) $\frac{2}{7}$ (e) $\frac{1}{8}$ (f) $\frac{2}{9}$
3. $\frac{3}{10}$ kg
4. $\frac{1}{12}$ litre
5. (a) $\frac{9}{10}$ litre   (b) $\frac{3}{5}$ litre
6. (a) $\frac{2}{5}$ (b) $\frac{1}{5}$ (c) $\frac{3}{5}$ (d) $\frac{1}{3}$ (e) $\frac{5}{7}$ (f) $\frac{1}{4}$
7. (a) $\frac{5}{8}$ kg   (b) $\frac{15}{32}$ kg
8. (a) $\frac{9}{20}$ m
9. (a) $\frac{1}{2}$ m   (b) $\frac{1}{4}$ m

Page 5   Home World

1. $1 \div \frac{1}{5}$ 2. $1 \div \frac{1}{8}$

   $= 1 \times \frac{5}{1}$ $= 1 \times \frac{8}{1}$

   $= \frac{5}{1}$ $= \frac{8}{1}$

   $= 5$ $= 8$

3. (a) 4 (b) 6 (c) 12 (d) $\frac{3}{5}$ (e) $\frac{3}{7}$ (f) $2\frac{1}{2}$
   (g) 6 (h) $1\frac{1}{2}$ (i) $1\frac{1}{3}$
4. 6 pieces
5. (a) 12 times   (b) 15 times

Page 6   Rational thinking

1. (a) Weavers Way 4 : 3, Main Avenue 1 : 3, Pennine Road 2 : 3
   (b) Weavers Way 3 : 4, Main Avenue 3 : 1, Pennine Road 3 : 2
2. (a) 4 : 3   (b) 3 : 4
3. (a) 3 : 7   (b) 7 : 3
4. (a) 5 : 2   (b) 2 : 5
5. (a) 8   (b) 6   (c) 4 : 3
6. (a) 1 : 2   (b) 5 : 2   (c) 2 : 3   (d) 2 : 3   (e) 2 : 3
   (f) 3 : 4   (g) 5 : 7   (h) 6 : 5   (i) 5 : 3   (j) 4 : 1
   (k) 25 : 1   (l) 1 : 2

Pages 7 and 8   Concrete examples

1. (a) 8   (b) 14   (c) 20   (d) 30
2. (a) 20   (b) 30   (c) 50   (d) 85
3. (a) 90   (b) 144   (c) 198   (d) 45
4. (a) 15   (b) 36   (c) 54   (d) 66
5. (a) 35   (b) 49   (c) 70   (d) 84
6. (a) 3 : 2   (b) • 800   • 1000   • 1220   • 1420
7. (a) 49   (b) 63   (c) 98   (d) 112
8. (a) 28 m³ of sand, 12 m³ of cement
   (b) 42 m³ of sand, 18 m³ of cement
   (c) 56 m³ of sand, 24 m³ of cement
   (d) 70 m³ of sand, 30 m³ of cement

9 (a) 9 m³ of sand, 15 m³ of cement
  (b) 21 m³ of sand, 35 m³ of cement
  (c) 27 m³ of sand, 45 m³ of cement
  (d) 33 m³ of sand, 55 m³ of cement
10 (a) 16 kg of compost, 24 kg of top soil
  (b) 24 kg of compost, 36 kg of top soil
  (c) 14 kg of compost, 21 kg of top soil
  (d) 30 kg of compost, 45 kg of top soil
11 4·5 m³ of white gravel, 20·5 m³ of red gravel
12 26·7 litres of paint, 13·3 litres of white spirit
13 (a) Myra receives £9000, John receives £12 000
  (b) Myra receives £24 000, John receives £32 000
  (c) Myra receives £0·6 million, John receives £0·8 million
14 (a) Myra receives £14 500, John receives £11 600
  (b) Myra receives £32 000, John receives £25 600
  (c) Myra receives £1 million, John receives £0·8 million
15 20 m³ of sand, 8 m³ of gravel, 4 m³ of cement

Page 9 Back to square one

Students do practical work.

Page 10 Packham's

1

Product name	Prism
Head Safe	Cube
Gale Force Tent	Triangular Prism
Fresh up Wipes	Hexagonal Prism
China Set	Cuboid
Mints	Cuboid
Tennis balls	Pentagonal Prism

2 Head Safe, 15 625 cm³
  Fresh up Wipes, 10 375 cm³
  China Set, 6000 cm³
  Mints, 1687·5 cm³
  Tennis balls, 240 cm³
3 (a) 15·9 m³ **(b)** 6·82 m³ **(c)** 4·55 m3 **(d)** 0·9 m³
4 Worksheet 1
5 • S, 6 cm³ • T, 1 cm³

Pages 11 and 12 The Daisy Chain

1 (a) 420 cm³ **(b)** 480 cm³ **(c)** 585 cm³
  (d) 648 cm³ **(e)** 625 cm³ **(f)** 455 cm³
2 (a) 250 cm³ **(b)** 112 cm³
3 (a) 600 cm³ **(b)** 48 cm by 32 cm by 12 cm high
  (c) 18 432 cm³ **(d)** 14 400 cm³ **(e)** 4032 cm³
4 Students own designs and calculations. The difference is always 4032 cm².
5 (a) 154 cm² **(b)** 13 cm²
6 (a) 216 cm² **(b)** 227 cm²
7 (a) 4832 cm³ **(b)** 6782 cm³
8 (a) 2460 cm³ **(b)** 311 cm³ **(c)** 2200 cm³
  (d) 1210 cm³
9 206 000 cm³
10 (a) 1 700 000 cm³ **(b)** 1700 l
11 (a) 1410 cm³ **(b)** 675 000 mm³
12 He should double the height.

Pages 13 and 14 Prism Play Centre

(a) • 13 500 cm³ • 13·5 l
(b) • 99 000 cm³ • 99 l
(c) • 69 120 cm³ • 69·12 l
(d) • 11 760 cm³ • 11·76 l
(a) 4050 cm² **(b)** 23 800 cm²
(c) 13 248 cm² **(d)** 4816 cm²
Worksheet 2

4 (a) • 157 cm • 11 800 cm²
  (b) • 62·8 cm • 5020 cm²
  (c) • 113 cm • 8820 cm²
  (d) • 314 cm • 21 980 cm²
5 (a) • 18 000 cm³ • 4400 cm²
  (b) • 16 500 cm³ • 4450 cm²
  (c) • 5280 cm² • 2880 cm²
  (d) • 173 000 cm³ • 17 600 cm²
6 30 cm

Page 15 Card calculators

1

Number	1	2	4	8
1	✔			
2		✔		
3	✔	✔		
4			✔	
5	✔		✔	
6		✔	✔	
7	✔	✔	✔	
8				✔
9	✔			✔
10		✔		✔
11	✔	✔		✔
12			✔	✔
13	✔		✔	✔
14		✔	✔	✔
15	✔	✔	✔	✔

2, 3 Student's own answers.
4 A number will appear on *Card A* if it is ticked in the column headed **1**.
  A number will appear on *Card B* if it is ticked in the column headed **2**, and so on.
5 (a)

Card E			
16	17	18	19
20	21	22	23
24	25	26	27
28	29	30	31

(b) Student's own tests.
6 (a)

Card B							
2	3	6	7	10	11	14	15
18	19	22	23	26	27	30	31
34	35	38	39	42	43	46	47
50	51	54	55	58	59	62	63

Card C							
4	5	6	7	12	13	14	15
20	21	22	23	28	29	30	31
36	37	38	39	44	45	46	47
52	53	54	55	60	61	62	63

Card E							
16	17	18	19	20	21	22	23
24	25	26	27	28	29	30	31
48	49	50	51	52	53	54	55
56	57	58	59	60	61	62	63

Card F							
32	33	34	35	36	37	38	39
40	41	42	43	44	45	46	47
48	49	50	51	52	53	54	55
56	57	58	59	60	61	62	63

(b) Student's own tests.

Page 16 Job hunting

1 £6656
2 £8700
3 (a) £9672 (b) £806
4 Syeda by £280
5 Shabana
6 £124
7 £133·50
8 Sabrina by £15·15
9 £3·45
10 Pam by 3p per hour

Page 17 Pay slips

1 October
2 R 004
3 (a) 350L (b) £73·08
4 (a) RT 654392 B (b) £52·74
5 £56·18
6 £182·00
7 £546·00
8 £40·00
9 £586·00
10 £404·00
11 Worksheet 3
12 (a) £93 (b) £99 (c) £85 (d) £483 (e) £453
13 Students' own estimates.

Page 18 Overtime

1 (a) £126 (b) £27 (c) £153
2 £158·76
3 £168
4 £166·26
5 £185·28
6 £287·64
7 £216·32

Page 19 On time

1 (a) 08·30 (b) 12·00 (c) 17·00
2 (a) Wednesday (b) Thursday
3 39·5 hours
4 £129·60
5 £134·40
6 Worksheet 4
7 £98·20
8 £69·63
9 £64·96
10 £292·95
11 4%

Page 20 Deductions

1 (a) £16·56 (b) £18·54 (c) £115·56 (d) £134·55
2 £7·82
3 £17·82
4 £14 257
5 £3587
6 (a) £5700·00 (b) £2255·00 (c) £451·00
7 (a) £7176·00 (b) £3427·00 (c) £731·75
8 £267·75

Page 21 Just the job

1 (a) £4.20 (b) £157·50
2 £173·25
3 4·42
4 £1442·00

Page 22 Premium prices

1 £915
2 £1304
3 £811·80
4 £562·80
5 £555·20
6 (a) £1148 (b) £1216·88
7 Students' own investigation.

5 (a) £171·72 (b) £119·76
6 (a) £42·80 (b) £74·60 (c) £166·10
7 (a) £21 300 (b) £14 847 (c) £3586·75
8 (a) £120·64 (b) £109·33
9 £235·34
10 £317·50
11 £112·45

Page 23 Planning for the future

1 (a) £2·10 (b) £12·60
2 £45·20
3 £9·45
4 £62·25
5 (a) Tariq £45·20 (b) Iqbal £40·80
   (c) He is older and so may make fewer payments while he is alive.
6 (a) £10·07 (b) 472 months (c) 65

Page 24 Chess challenges

1 A possible solution:
   A7, B5, C3, D1, E6, F8, G2, H4
2 204 squares
3 Students investigate Knight's Tour problem.

Pages 25 and 26 Fair play?

1 (a) $\frac{1}{6}$ (b) $\frac{1}{12}$ (c) $\frac{1}{4}$ (d) $\frac{1}{3}$

2 (a) $\frac{1}{4}$ (b) $\frac{1}{16}$ (c) $\frac{1}{2}$ (d) $\frac{3}{16}$

3 (a) $\frac{1}{4}$ (b) $\frac{5}{36}$ (c) $\frac{1}{36}$ (d) $\frac{7}{12}$

4 (a) $\frac{1}{16}$ (b) Skill is a factor.

5 (a) $\frac{2}{15}$

6 (a) $\frac{1}{10}$ (b) $\frac{1}{5}$ (c) $\frac{3}{25}$ (d) $\frac{1}{10}$

7 (a) $\frac{1}{9}$ (b) $\frac{1}{4}$ (c) $\frac{1}{12}$ (d) $\frac{3}{16}$

8 (a) $\frac{1}{12}$ (b) $\frac{1}{12}$ (c) $\frac{1}{6}$

9 (a) Students tree diagram showing a total of 36 possible combinations
   (b) $\frac{1}{36}$

10 (a) There are 36 possible combinations.
   (b) Totals are 2, 3, 4, 5, 6, 7, 8, 9, 10, 11, 12
   (c) P(7) = $\frac{1}{6}$ P(10) = $\frac{1}{12}$ P(12) = $\frac{1}{36}$ P(5) = $\frac{1}{9}$

Page 27 Probabilities of this and that

1 (a) $\frac{1}{2}$ (b) $\frac{1}{6}$

(c)

head, 1	head, 2	head, 3	head, 4	head, 5	head, 6
tail, 1	tail, 2	tail, 3	tail, 4	tail, 5	tail, 6

(d) $\frac{1}{12}$

2 (a) $\frac{1}{2}$ **(b)** $\frac{1}{4}$

(c)

head, R	head, G	head, W	head, Y
tail, R	tail, G	tail, W	tail, Y

(d) $\frac{1}{8}$

3 (a) $\frac{1}{3}$ **(b)** $\frac{1}{6}$

(c)

red, 1	red, 2	red, 3	red, 4	red, 5	red, 6
blue, 1	blue, 2	bluel, 3	blue, 4	blue, 5	blue, 6
white, 1	white, 2	white, 3	white, 4	white, 5	white, 6

(d) $\frac{1}{18}$

4 (a)

	P(1st event)	P(2nd event)	P(1st and 2nd event)
Problem 1	$\frac{1}{2}$	$\frac{1}{6}$	$\frac{1}{12}$
Problem 2	$\frac{1}{2}$	$\frac{1}{4}$	$\frac{1}{8}$
Problem 3	$\frac{1}{3}$	$\frac{1}{6}$	$\frac{1}{18}$

(b) P(1st event) × P(2nd event) = P(1st and 2nd events)

5 (a) • $\frac{1}{4}$ • $\frac{1}{5}$ **(b)** $\frac{1}{20}$

6 (a) • $\frac{1}{2}$ • $\frac{1}{7}$ **(b)** $\frac{1}{14}$

7 (a) • $\frac{1}{6}$ • $\frac{1}{7}$ **(b)** $\frac{1}{42}$

8 (a) • $\frac{1}{4}$ • $\frac{2}{7}$ **(b)** $\frac{2}{28}$ **or** $\frac{1}{14}$

Page 28   Probabilities of this *or* that

1 (a) $\frac{1}{6}$ **(b)** $\frac{1}{6}$ **(c)** $\frac{2}{6}$ or $\frac{1}{3}$

2 (a) $\frac{1}{7}$ **(b)** $\frac{1}{7}$ **(c)** $\frac{2}{7}$

3 (a) $\frac{4}{52}$ or $\frac{1}{13}$ **(b)** $\frac{12}{52}$ or $\frac{3}{13}$ **(c)** $\frac{16}{52}$ or $\frac{4}{13}$

4 (a) $\frac{4}{11}$ **(b)** $\frac{1}{11}$ **(c)** $\frac{5}{11}$

5 Students' own check.

6 (a) • $\frac{25}{100}$ or $\frac{1}{4}$

    • $\frac{50}{100}$ or $\frac{1}{2}$

    • $\frac{12}{100}$ or $\frac{3}{25}$

    • $\frac{13}{100}$

(b) • $\frac{75}{100}$ or $\frac{3}{4}$

    • $\frac{25}{100}$ or $\frac{1}{4}$

    • $\frac{63}{100}$

    • $\frac{75}{100}$ or $\frac{3}{4}$

    • $\frac{100}{100}$ or 1

7 (a) $\frac{19}{50}$ **(b)** $\frac{23}{50}$ **(c)** $\frac{8}{50}$ or $\frac{4}{25}$ **(d)** $\frac{42}{50}$ or $\frac{21}{25}$

Pages 29 and 30   A problem shared

1 $(x + 3)(x + 1) = x^2 + 4x + 3$

2 $x^2 + 4x - 5$

3 Yes, she has $\frac{1}{10}$ kg left for her daughter.

4 6 full jugs, $\frac{1}{2}$ litre of water

5 (a) 200 g   **(b)** 150 g

6 (a) 506 cm³, 502 cm³   **(b)** 381 cm², 351 cm²
   (c) Students own choice with reasons.

7

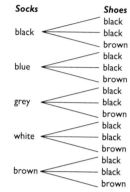

P(socks and shoes of the same colour) = $\frac{3}{15}$ or $\frac{1}{5}$

8 £138

9 950 cc

10 (a) • $\frac{13}{20}$ • 0·65   **(b)** 35%

11 Motorcare is the cheaper policy, by £8·12.

12 $\frac{1}{6}$

13 The 9 inch pizza costs 6·13 pence per square centimetre. The 12 inch pizza is better value as it costs 4·33 pence per square centimetre.

14 (a) 150°   **(b)** 135°

15

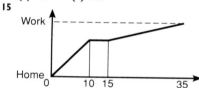

Page 31   Keep in line

1 (a) • $m = 4 \times s$
   • m

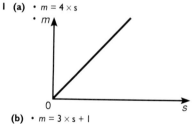

(b) • $m = 3 \times s + 1$
   • m

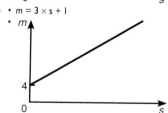

2 (a) $s = 8 \times 1 + 4$

(b)

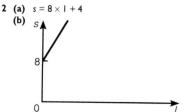

3 (a) $V = 2 \cdot 5 \times l$
(b) A straight line through the origin.
(c)

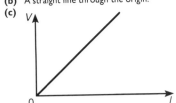

4 (a) $V = 2 \times t + 10$
(b) A straight line through the (0, 10).
(c)

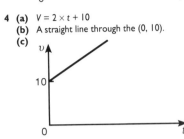

Page 32 Quadratics and parabolas

1 (a)

(b) • $t = p^2 + 1$
•

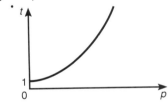

(c) • $t = p^2 + 5$
•

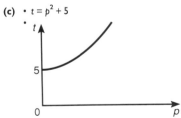

2 (a)

x	⁻4	⁻3	⁻2	⁻1	0	1	2	3	4
y	16	9	4	1	0	1	4	9	16

(b)

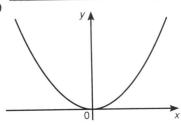

3 (a) $h = d^2 + 4$
(b) A parabola through (0, 4).
(c)

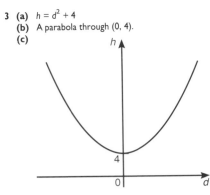

Page 33 Zoe's cubes

1 (b)

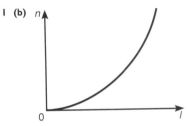

2 (a)

x	⁻4	⁻3	⁻2	⁻1	0	1	2	3	4
y	⁻64	⁻27	⁻8	⁻1	0	1	8	27	64

(b)

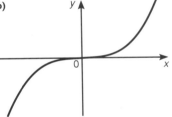

3 (a)

x	⁻4	⁻3	⁻2	⁻1	0	1	2	3	4
y	⁻60	⁻23	⁻4	3	4	5	12	31	68

(b)

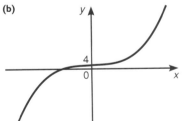

4 (a)

x	⁻4	⁻3	⁻2	⁻1	0	1	2	3	4
y	⁻54	⁻17	2	9	10	11	18	37	74

(b)

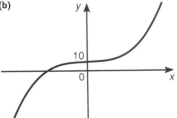

5 (a)

x	⁻4	⁻3	⁻2	⁻1	0	1	2	3	4
y	⁻74	⁻37	⁻18	⁻11	⁻10	⁻9	⁻2	17	54

(b)

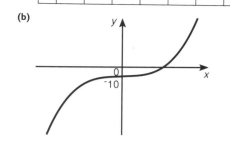

Page 34 Divide and rule

1 (a)

Breadth in cm (b)	1	2	3	4	5	6
Length in cm (l)	24	12	8	6	4·8	4

(b) Students own check.

(c)

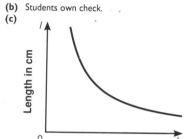

2 (a)

Speed in km/h (s)	10	20	30	40	50	60
Time in hours (t)	6	3	2	1·5	1·2	1

(b) $t = \frac{60}{s}$

(c)

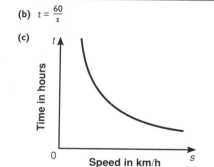

3 (a)

Seat price in £ (p)	3	4	6	8	12	16
Number of visits (v)	16	12	8	6	4	3

(b) $v = \frac{48}{p}$

(c)

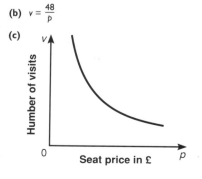

4 (a)

x	1	2	3	4	5	6	7	8	10
y	1	0.5	0.33	0.25	0.2	0.17	0.14	0.13	0.1

(b) A hyperbola

(c)

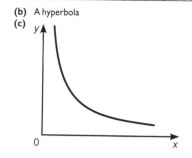

5 (a) $I = \frac{18}{R}$

(b) A hyperbola

(c)

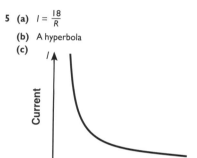

6 (a) $P = \frac{45}{V}$

(b) A hyperbola

(c)

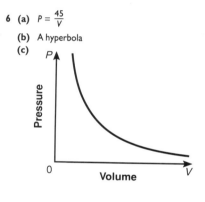

Page 35 Matchmakers

1, D   2, I   3, F   4, J   5, A
6, E   7, H   8, G   9, B   10, C

Page 36 Getting the point

1 (a) (2,12), (8,42), (12,62)
  (b) • (0,2) • (1,7) • (7,37) • (10,52)
2 (a) (2,7), (⁻1,4)
  (b) • (0,3) • (1,4) • (⁻3,12) • (4,19)
3 (a) (3,7), (⁻10,98)
  (b) • (0,⁻2) • (1,⁻1) • (2,2) • (⁻3,7)
4 (a) (3,26), (4,63), (⁻3,⁻28)
  (b) • (0,⁻1) • (1,0) • (⁻2,⁻9) • (5,124)
5 (a) (1,6), (⁻2,⁻3)
  (b) • (0,5) • (2,13) • (⁻3,⁻22) • (5,130)
6 (a) (2,15), (5,6), (0·5,60)
  (b) • (1,30) • (6,5) • (10,3) • (12,2·5)

Pages 37 and 38   Red Dragon Transport

1 (a) 15 minutes
   (b) via Gloucester
   (c) 6 vans
   (d) • 3 vans   • 2 vans
   (e) C_3 and A_3
2 (a) 5 h 15 min   (b) 2 h
   (c) 7 hr 25 min
3 (a) 50 mins   (b) 5 h
   (c) 3 h 10 min   (d) 5 h 5 mins
4 (a) 7 h 10 min   (b) 4 h 15 min
   (c) 7 h 30 min   (d) 7 h 25 min
   (e) 9 h 50 min
5 (a) 11 h 35 min   (b) 8 h 45 min
   (c) 5 h 55 min   (d) 11 h 55 min
6 (a) 2 h 45 min   (b) 13 h 5 min
   (c) 4 h 45 min   (d) 5 h 50 min
7 Van A_2 leaves at 0140.
8 Van C_3 takes 15 h 50 min.
9 (a) 3 h 40 min   (b) 10 h
   (c) 8 h 35 min   (d) 11 h 20 min
   (e) 12 h 50 min
10 (a) 4·45 pm   (b) 1210
    (c) 0045 next day   (d) 2·40 am next day
    (e) 1445   (f) 6·35 am next day
    (g) 2335
11 1710 next day

Page 39   Timing it right

1 (a) 2 h 30 min   (b) 3 h 45 min   (c) 42 min
   (d) 1 h 12 min   (e) 4 h 54 min   (f) 2 h 18 min
2 (a) 2·6 h   (b) 1·1 h   (c) 3·83 h
   (d) 5·05 h   (e) 2·33 h   (f) 4·47 h
3 (a) 50 mph (b) 48 mph (c) 40 mph (d) 42 mph
   (e) 46 mph (f) 40 mph (g) 48 mph (h) 40 mph
4 Cardiff – Glasgow 44 mph
   Glasgow – Leeds 40 mph
   Leeds – Cardiff 45 mph
   Cardiff – Swansea 50 mph
   Swansea – Milford Haven 40 mph
   Milford Haven – Cardiff 30 mph
   Cardiff – Dover 28 mph
   Dover – Cardiff 35 mph
5 Cardiff – Portsmouth 56 km/h
   Portsmouth – Caen 28 km/h
   Caen – Paris 72 km/h
   Paris – Roscoff 50 km/h
   Roscoff – Plymouth 30 km/h
   Plymouth – Cardiff 70 km/h

Page 40   On the right road

1 (a) 3 h   (b) 4 h
   (c) 8 h 30 min   (d) 1 h 45 min
2 (a) 3 h   (b) 4 h
   (c) 2 h 30 min   (d) 1 h 30 min
   (e) 1 h 45 min   (f) 48 min
   (g) 2 h 12 min   (h) 1 h 12 min
3 11.30 am
4 No. He will arrive at 7.55 am.
5 (a) 273 miles   (b) 242 miles   (c) 204 miles
6 Edinburgh – Newcastle 105 miles
   Newcastle – Leeds 92 miles
   Leeds – Nottingham 72 miles
   Nottingham – Birmingham 52·5 miles
   Birmingham – Cardiff 106 miles
7 (a) 10 m/s   (b) 15 m/s   (c) 25 m/s
8 (a) 22 m   (b) 56 m   (c) 100 m

Page 41   On the road

1 (a) • 25 miles   • 11 miles   (b) 16 minutes
2 (a) 2 miles   (b) 10 minutes
3 (a) 80 miles   (b) Pembroke to Carmarthen
   (c) 18 miles   (d) 108 minutes
4 (a) 90 minutes   (b) 66 miles
   (c) 6 minutes   (d) Swansea to Merthyr Tydfil
5 (a) • 60 miles   • 30 miles
   (b) 45 minutes   (c) 20 miles

Page 42   Speed it up

1 (a) 30 miles   (b) 30 minutes   (c) 60 mph
2 (a) 15 miles   (b) 20 minutes   (c) 45 mph
3 (a) 65 miles   (b) 80 minutes   (c) 49 mph
4 (a)

From	To	Distance	Time	Speed
Carmarthen	Llanelli	10	15	40
Llanelli	Swansea	15	20	45
Carmarthen	Swansea	25	35	43

   (b) 2·50 pm
5 (a) 46 mph   (b) 60 mph

Page 43   Count the miles

1 (a) 146 miles   (b) 433 miles
   (c) 254 miles   (d) 394 miles
2, 3, 4, 5 Worksheet 5
6 Student's own map showing mileages.

Page 44   Freight costs

1 (a) £40   (b) £110   (c) £472
2 (a) Claire £5·90 per hour
        Sam £6·50 per hour
        James £9·30 per hour
   (b) £203
3 (a) £46   (b) £173   (c) £305
4 £35
5 Economy
6 Standard for 2 days
7 Mini × 3, Economy × 1, Mega × 2 or Economy × 2, Standard × 1, Mega × 2

Page 45   Hexaflexagon

Students do practical work.

Page 46   Playing with trigonometry

1 Triangle Q: ratio = 0·25
   Triangle R: ratio = 0·25
2 Worksheet 7, question 1.
3 (a) 0·375   (b) 2·5   (c) 3
   (d) 0·6   (e) 0·222   (f) 1·143

Page 47   Naming the sides

1 (a) ED   (b) PR   (c) SU   (d) YZ
2 (a) AB   (b) LN   (c) ST   (d) VW
3 (a) HJ   (b) YZ   (c) DE   (d) CD
4 (a) 0·4   (b) 0·85   (c) 1·4   (d) 1·4
   (e) 2·25   (f) 0·625   (g) 0·75   (h) 2·4

Page 48 A calculator tan

1. (a) 0·364 (b) 1·327 (c) 9·514
   (d) 3·078 (e) 0·687 (f) 2·633
   (g) 1 (h) 13·300 (i) 0
2. $a = 29.9°$ $b = 52.9°$ $c = 42.0°$ $d = 45.0°$
   $e = 39.1°$ $f = 76.4°$ $g = 88.2°$ $h = 15.4°$
   $i = 75.6°$ $j = 60.0°$
3. (a) 51·3° (b) 38·7° (c) 35·5° (d) 22·6°
4. 56·8°
5. 70·7°

Page 49 Another angle on trig

1. (a) 0·454 (b) 0·629 (c) 0·866
   (d) 0·980 (e) 0·995 (f) 0·543
2. $a = 30°$ $b = 51.7°$ $c = 60.1°$ $d = 67.2°$
   $e = 34.2°$ $f = 18.0°$ $g = 45°$ $h = 29.6°$
   $i = 54.9°$ $j = 5.7°$
3. $a = 0848$ $b = 33.7$ $c = 53.1°$ $d = 39.5°$
4. (a) 0·848 (b) 0·545 (c) 0·585
   (d) 0·707 (e) 0·277 (f) 0·045
5. $a = 37.8°$ $b = 57.1°$ $c = 33.1°$ $d = 39.6°$
   $e = 68.5°$ $f = 87.9°$ $g = 0.0°$ $h = 12.3°$
   $i = 60.0°$ $j = 90.0°$
6. $a = 53.1°$ $b = 38.2°$ $c = 56.7°$ $d = 29.6°$

Page 50 Child's play?

1. Worksheet 7, question 2.
2. (a) 25·8° (b) 45° (c) 14·5°
   (d) 68·8° (e) 68·2° (f) 27·3°
3. 22·6°
4. 56·0°

Pages 51 and 52 Flying the flag

1. Worksheet 8, question 1
2. (a) 5·5 n (b) 5·2 m (c) 6·8 m
3. Worksheet 8, question 2
4. (a) 5·9 m (b) 6·4 m (c) 9·0 m
5. Worksheet 8, question 3
6. (a) 1·9 m (b) 1·3 m (c) 1·8 m
7. Worksheet 8, question 4
8. (a) 3·8 m (b) 9·1 cm (c) 1·0 m (d) 54·5 mm
   (e) 2·6 m (f) 3·2 m (g) 8·0 mm (h) 4·3 cm
9. 6 cm
10. 693 m
11. (a) Student's own sketch (b) 1·8 m
12. 31·1 cm
13. 26·4 m
14. (a) Student's own sketch (b) 3·2 cm
15. 15·6 m
16. (a) Students' own sketch
    (b) 23·9 m

Page 53 Figure it out

1. 346 feet
2. 52·9°
3. (a) Students' own sketch (b) 0·5 m
4. 38·2°
5. (a) Students' own sketch (b) 16·3 km
6. 3·5 m
7. 5·3°
8. 7·1 cm
9. (a) 63·4° (b) 18·4°
10. 78·5°
11. (a) Students' own sketch (b) 3·6 miles, 033·7°

Page 54 A class act

1. (a) 7 (b) 24
2. (a) 18 (b) 27
3. (a) (b) Worksheet 9 (c) 19 (d) 31
4. (a) (b) Worksheet 9 (c) 28 (d) 18
5. (a) (b) Worksheet 10 (c) 14
6. (a) (b) Worksheet 10 (c) •2 • 20 (d) 31

Pages 55 and 56 Keeping them in order

1. (a) 7, 4, 9, 5
   (b) 23, 19·5, 28·5, 9
   (c) 6, 3, 9, 6
   (d) 22, 9·5, 38·5, 29
2. (a) 25, 23 and 26, 3 (b) 11, 10 and 12, 2
3. (a) 19, 11·5 and 24, 12·5 (b) 38, 24 and 50, 26

Pages 57 and 58 Radio Dunedin

1. (a) 2 h 55 min (b) 9 min (c) 10·3%
2. $\frac{1}{30}$
3. 6 min 5 s
4. 95·7, 97·3
5. *In and around:* 32 cm, *Ages and ages:* 22 years, *Boxed in:* 58 boxes
   Self raising: 6 days, *Hot stuff:* 25°
6. (a) 2 h (b) 15 min (c) 30 min (d) 3 h
7. (a) FM (b) Saturday
8. (a) 21 min (b) 3:2 (c) 10%
9. 2 h 33 min
10. (a) 52% (b) $\frac{1}{3}$
11. (a)

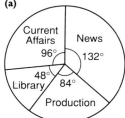

(b) Current affairs. Just over 25% of the staff earn over 40% of the wages.

Pages 59 and 60 Advertise live on 96·5

1. Mental Motors £60,
   Freezar Meats £130,
   Barrs Self Drive £870
   Simpson's Furnishing £115
2. 511 890
3. (a) £1173·83 (b) £8395·38 (c) £64·63
4. (a) £49 (b) £72 (c) £90
   (d) £9 (e) £30 (f) £18
5. £438
6. (a) • 0600 – 1200 • 2400 – 0600
   (b) $C = 0.1t + 1$
7. (a)

Time (s)	10	20	30	40	50	60
Cost (£)	70	90	110	130	150	170

Time	10	20	30	40	50	60
Cost (£)	40	80	120	160	200	240

(b) Student's own graph.
(c) Imran should use Rate B if he requires airtime of less than or equal to 25 seconds. Use Rate A if the airtime is greater than or equal to 25 seconds

1 (a)

Leg	Bearing	Distance (km)
H–F	340°	6·75
F–N	200°	6·25
N–S	140°	21·75
S–M	040°	5
M–H	275°	19·5

   (b) 59·25 km   (c) 39·5 km/h
2 290 m
3 618 m
4 (a) 30 litres (b) 60 min   (c) $F = \frac{t}{3}$ or $\frac{1}{3}t$
   where f is the fuel in litres and t is the time in min
5 (a) 9·40 am (b) 8·6 mph

Page 62   Thor's Challenge

1 1 Adult £4, Child £1·50
2 (a) 504 m   (b) 5·6 m/s
3 (a) 11·3 m   (b) 2·0 m
4 6 ways
5 7 steps
6 (a) 13·61   (b) 8

Pages 63 and 64   More problems

1 73·7°
2 9 h 20 min
3 32
4 (a) 42   (b) no   (c) graph Z
5 0755
6 Yes, it is 26·5 feet high
7 Yes, 93 km/h
8 144 sheep
9 (a) 5·66 m (b) 33·88 m
10 (a) 10   (b) 5   (c) 4
11 (a) 12x   (b) 36 cm   (c) 6
12 (a) 4   (b) 7   (c) £10

Pages 65 and 66   Locating a locus

Worksheets 11, 12 and 13.

Page 67   Crack the code

$a = 270, b = 180, c = 30, d = 1$
Mystery number = 2

Page 68   All wrapped up

1 $5r + 75 = 2r + 195, r = 40$
2 (a) $x = 3$ (b) $r = 7$ (c) $q = 5$ (d) $r = 7$
   (e) $v = 3$ (f) $p = 20$ (g) $q = 3$ (h) $y = 4$
   (i) $i = 6$ (j) $t = 7$ (k) $h = 5$ (l) $v = 0$
   (m) $d = 8$ (n) $c = 2$

Page 69   In the balance

1 $3w > 150, w > 50$
   Each box weighs more than 50 g.
2 $4w < 1000, w < 250$
   Each box weighs less than 250 g.

3 $8w > 2400, w > 300$
   Each box weighs more than 300 g.
4 $12w < 480, w < 40$
   Each box weighs less than 40 g.
5 (a) $a > 4$ (b) $f < 16$ (c) $c \leq 8$ (d) $x \leq 4$
   (e) $y < 4$ (f) $g < 3$ (g) $x \geq 2$ (h) $t > 2$
   (i) $d < 9$ (j) $b \geq 3$ (k) $n > 3$ (l) $d < 4$
   (m) $x < 1$ (n) $w \leq 4$ (o) $p > 3$ (p) $w \geq 1$
6 $5w + 100 > 3w + 300, w > 100$
   Each box weighs more than 100 g.
7 $9w + 200 < 6w + 800, w < 200$
   Each box weighs less than 200 g.

Page 70   Christmas hampers

1 $3(3w + 2c) = 9w + 6c$
2 (a) $12b + 6$ (b) $21k + 63$ (c) $30a - 48$
   (d) $24 + 2v$ (e) $81 - 18k$ (f) $65x + 35$
   (g) $96 - 84p$ (h) $42f + 91$ (i) $28 - 63f$
3 (a) $w = 3$ (b) $x = 2$ (c) $y = 5$ (d) $f = 4$
   (e) $a = 1$ (f) $g = 3$ (g) $p = 6$ (h) $r = 2$
   (i) $x = 10$ (j) $b = 3$ (k) $c = 0$ (l) $b = 15$
   (m) $f = 0$ (n) $w = 2$ (o) $y = 3$ (p) $m = 2$
4 (a) $x = 10$ (b) $y = 36$ (c) $k = 30$ (d) $a = 35$
   (e) $p = 56$ (f) $r = 99$ (g) $b = 6$ (h) $h = 12$
   (i) $g = 16$ (j) $g = 20$ (k) $t = 8$ (l) $w = 16$
   (m) $v = 64$ (n) $b = 50$ (o) $b = 10$ (p) $m = 8$
   (q) $y = 80$ (r) $k = 12$
5 (a) $w = 3$ (b) $d = 13$ (c) $f = 8$ (d) $u = 8$
   (e) $h = 9$ (f) $d = 3$

Pages 71 and 72   Under Raps

1 (a) C   (b) V   (c) D   (d) p
2 (a) •£26 •£57 •£36 •£44 •£171
   (b) •£16 •£10 •£68 •£37 •£144
3 (a) £59   (b) £17   (c) £94
   (d) £32   (e) £181   (f) £131
4 (a) $h = c - 7$ (b) $h = f - 9$ (c) $h = r - 13$
   (d) $h = p - d$ (e) $h = f - r$ (f) $h = u - i$
   (g) $h = k + 4$ (h) $h = u + 8$ (i) $h = s + 10$
   (j) $h = b + t$ (k) $h = e + u$ (l) $h = w + t$
   (m) $h = j - 4$ (n) $h = w - p$ (o) $h = d - e$
5 (a) •£12 •£54 •£60 •£144
   (b) •4 h •7 h •12 h •9 h •20 h
6 (a) $T = \frac{H}{7}$ (b) $T = \frac{H}{3}$ (c) $T = \frac{H}{9}$ (d) $T = \frac{H}{15}$
7 (a) £300   (b) $T = \frac{W}{15}$ (c) 16 hours
8 (a) £102   (b) £15 per hour   (c) 9 hours
9 (a) $s = \frac{d}{t}$ (b) $t = \frac{d}{s}$ (c) $i = \frac{v}{r}$
   (d) $r = \frac{v}{i}$ (e) $d = \frac{c}{\pi}$ (f) $g = \frac{p}{10h}$
10 (a) $b = \frac{2A}{h}$ (b) 50 cm
11 (a) $b = \frac{v}{lh}$ (b) 14 cm
12 (a) 30 cm   (b) 25 cm   (c) 65 cm
13 (a) $r = \sqrt{\frac{A}{\pi}}$ (b) • $r = 10$ • $r = 3$
14 (a) $r = \sqrt{\frac{V}{\pi h}}$ (b) $r = 5$

Pages 73 and 74   On the carpet

1 (a) $l^2 = 16, l = 4$ m   (b) $l^2 = 81, l = 9$ m   (c) $l^2 = 169, l = 13$ m
   (d) $l^2 = 49, l = 7$ m   (e) $l^2 = 4, l = 2$ m   (f) $l^2 = 225, l = 15$ m
2 (a) 25   (b) 64   (c) 9   (d) 100   (e) 16   (f) 81
3 (a) $x = \pm3$ (b) $p = \pm11$ (c) $a = \pm2$
   (d) $w = \pm1$

4 (a) $x = \pm 3\cdot 74$ (b) $c = \pm 5\cdot 48$ (c) $t = \pm 2\cdot 45$
  (d) $g = \pm 7\cdot 42$ (e) $v = \pm 4\cdot 88$ (f) $s = \pm 0\cdot 866$
5 (a) $l^2 + 4 = 29, l = 5$ m   (b) $l^2 + 9 = 45, l = 6$ m
6 (a) $l^2 - 4 = 12, l = 4$ m   (b) $l^2 - 25 = 56, l = 9$ m
7 (a) $x = \pm 8$ (b) $f = \pm 9$ (c) $r = \pm 4$ (d) $v = \pm 4$
  (e) $b = \pm 10$ (f) $b = \pm 12$ (g) $d = \pm 8$ (h) $p = \pm 6$
8 (a) $5l^2 = 245, l = 7$ m   (b) $3l^2 = 243, l = 9$ m
  (c) $6l^2 = 96, l = 4$ m
9 (a) $x = \pm 5$ (b) $s = \pm 4$ (c) $c = \pm 2$ (d) $y = \pm 3$
  (e) $p = 1$ (f) $v = 5$ (g) $f = \pm 3$ (h) $s = \pm 8$

Page 75   On the carpet

1 (a) $x = \pm 5$ (b) $v = \pm 4$ (c) $c = \pm 1$
  (d) $p = \pm 5$ (e) $d = \pm 6$ (f) $c = \pm 3$
2 (a) $b = \pm 6\cdot 48$ (b) $h = \pm 7\cdot 62$ (c) $v = 9\cdot 17$
  (d) $c = \pm 2\cdot 83$ (e) $f = \pm 3\cdot 46$ (f) $t = \pm 2\cdot 83$
  (g) $b = \pm 3\cdot 61$ (h) $t = \pm 3\cdot 02$
3 (a) $x = 4$ (b) $x = 8$ (c) $x = 3$
  (d) $x = 10$ (e) $x = 6$ (f) $x = 7$
4 (a) $x = 2\cdot 5$ (b) $x = 3\cdot 1$ (c) $x = 4\cdot 8$ (d) $x = 4\cdot 8$
  (e) $x = 7\cdot 6$ (f) $x = 9\cdot 2$ (g) $x = 11$ (h) $x = 6\cdot 3$
5 $9\cdot 49$ cm

Page 76   Plot the dot

Students do practical work.

Pages 77 and 78   Chemical breakdown

1 (a) 2:1   (b) 2000   (c) 2500   (d) • 2400 • 1200
2 (a) $\dfrac{8}{9}$ (b) $\dfrac{1}{9}$
3 56 g of calcium oxide, 44 g of carbon dioxide.
4 25·71 g
5 (a) 700 kg   (b) 1429 kg
6 (a) $\dfrac{2}{5}$ (b) $\dfrac{3}{25}$ (c) $\dfrac{12}{25}$
7 1·6 g
8 (a) • $\dfrac{3}{7}$ • $\dfrac{4}{7}$ (b) • 42·9% • 57·1%   (c) 14·14 g
9 (a) • $\dfrac{3}{11}$ • $\dfrac{8}{11}$ (b) • 27·3% • 72·7%   (c) 15·3 g
10 Methane 1:4, Ethane 1:3, Propane 3:8, Butane 2:5, Pentane 5:12
11 (a) C_4H_{10} (b) C_6H_{14} (c) C_8H_{18}
12 (a)

Hydrocarbon	Mass of carbon	Mass of hydrogen	Molecular mass
Methane	12 units	4 units	16 units
Ethane	24 units	6 units	30 units
Propane	36 units	8 units	44 units
Butane	48 units	10 units	58 units
Pentane	60 units	12 units	72 units

  (b) • 3:1 • 9:2 • 5:1   (c) • 20% • 17·2% • 16·7%
13 (a) • $\dfrac{1}{5}$ • $\dfrac{4}{5}$ (b) • 20% • 80%
14 (a) • $\dfrac{2}{5}$ • $\dfrac{1}{15}$ • $\dfrac{8}{15}$ (b) • 40% • 6·7% • 53·3%

Pages 79 and 80   Formulations

1 (a) Carbon, Aluminium, Plutonium, Lead, Bromine, Mercury, Radon, Krypton
  (b) Krypton, Radon, Bromine, Mercury, Lead, Aluminium, Plutonium
2 (a) 1810°C (b) 66°C   (c) 396°C   (d) 5°C   (e) 9°C
3 (a) • 2·7 g/cm^3 3·5 g/cm^3 • 2·2 g/cm^3 • 11·3 g/cm^3
  (b) Lead, Carbon, Aluminium, Krypton
4 (a) • 266°K • 600°K • 234°K • 913°K
  (b) −273°C

5 (a) Iron 3273°K   Platinum 4803°K
      Xenon 165°K   Neon 27°K
  (b) −459.4°F
6 (a) α 35 ms^{-1}, β 92 ms^{-1}, χ −82 ms^{-1}, γ −26 ms^{-1}
  (b) • 2·1 ms^{-2} • 4·2 ms^{-2}
7 (a) 5790   (b) 5640   (c) 41 800
8 (a) 0·8   (b) 0·6
9 (a) 1·2   (b) 0·6

Page 81   Much ado about Nothings

1 (a) The height of Mount Everest is about 10^4 metres.
  (b) Man has inhabited the earth for about 10^5 years.
2 (a) 10^6 (b) 10^9 (c) 10^7 (d) 10^{18}
3 (a) The mass of 1 cubic metre of water is 1000 kg.
  (b) The amount of energy discharged in a flash of lightning is 1000 000 000 Joules.
  (c) The radius of the galaxy is about 10 000 000 000 000 000 metres.
4 (a) 1000 000   (b) 1000 000 000 000   (c) 100 000 000
  (d) 100 000 000 000 000
5 (a) The human ear cannot hear above about 2×10^4 Hertz.
  (b) The radius of the Earth is about 5×10^6 metres
  (c) The mass of the Earth is about 6×10^{24} kg.
6 (a) 3×10^6 (b) 5×10^4 (c) 9×10^8
  (d) 2×10^{10} (e) 7×10^9 (f) 8×10^{15}
7 (a) The speed of light is about 300 000 000 m/s.
  (b) The age of the Earth is about 6000 000 000 years.
  (c) The energy released by an earthquake can be of the order of 400 000 000 000 000 000 Joules.
8 (a) 200 000   (b) 500 000 000
  (c) 90 000 000 000 000   (d) 7000 000 000 000 000

Page 82   Planetary Fax

1 (a) $4\cdot 007 \times 10^4$ (b) $2\cdot 168 \times 10^5$ (c) $2\cdot 28 \times 10^8$
  (d) $1\cdot 08 \times 10^8$ (e) $4\cdot 37 \times 10^6$ (f) $2\cdot 3 \times 10$
2 (a) Uranus   (b) Jupiter   (c) Pluto
  (d) Jupiter
3 (a) • $1\cdot 52 \times 10^5$ • $1\cdot 53 \times 10^4$ (b) Neptune
4 (a) • $4\cdot 497 \times 10^9$ • $5\cdot 889 \times 10^9$ (b) $1\cdot 402 \times 10^9$
5 (a) • $2\cdot 22 \times 10^6$ • 4×10^4 (b) The sun has a greater mass.
6 (a) $a = 3\cdot 8, n = 4$ (b) $a = 1\cdot 16, n = 5$

Page 83   Pointed answers

1 (a) The thickness of this page is about 10^{-4} m.
  (b) A camera shutter speed can be 10^{-2} second.
  (c) The radius of a nucleus is about 10^{-14} m.
2 (a) 10^{-10} (b) 10^{-7} (c) 10^{-15} (d) 10^{-20}
3 (a) Microwave radiation can have a wavelength of 0·001 m.
  (b) A nanometre is 0·000 000 001 of a metre.
  (c) The wavelength of visible light is between about 0·000 0001 m and 0·000 000 01
4 (a) 0·000 01   (b) 0·1
  (c) 0·000 000 001   (d) 0·000 000 000 001
5 (a) Some X-rays have a wavelength of 5×10^{-10} m.
  (b) One second is equivalent to $3\cdot 169 \times 10^{-8}$ of a year.
  (c) The Bohr radius of an atom is $5\cdot 29 \times 10^{-11}$ m.
6 (a) 4×10^{-4} (b) $5\cdot 6 \times 10^{-6}$ (c) $3\cdot 24 \times 10^{-2}$
  (d) $7\cdot 88 \times 10^{-10}$ (e) $1\cdot 03 \times 10^{-5}$ (f) $9\cdot 008 \times 10^{-7}$
  (g) $2\cdot 46 \times 10^{-1}$ (h) $2\cdot 89 \times 10^6$ (i) $4\cdot 56 \times 10^{11}$
  (j) $9\cdot 06 \times 10^5$ (k) $3\cdot 5 \times 10^{16}$
7 (a) The mass of a proton is 0·000 000 000 000 000 000 000 000 001 673 kg
  (b) The charge of an electron is 0·000 000 000 000 000 000 160 2 C
  (c) The Avogadro number is 602 300 000 000 000 000 000 000
  (d) The speed of light is 299 800 000 m/s
  (e) The mass of a proton is equal to the mass of 1840 electrons.

1 (a) 2.4×10^9 m (b) 4.5×10^8 m (c) 2.04×10^9 m
  (d) 2.1×10^{10} m
2 (a) 4.816×10^{24} (b) 1.505×10^{24} (c) 3.01×10^{25}
3 (a) 1.38×10^5 (b) 1.656×10^{10} (c) 1.8867×10^3
  (d) 4.6547×10^{28} (e) 2.00866×10^9 (f) 1.424×10^{13}
4 (a) 2.49×10^{21} m (b) 1.05×10^{25} m (c) 2.129×10^{36} m
  (d) 2.0025×10^{44} m
5 (a) 1.38×10^{13} (b) 1.656×10^{13} (c) 3.5793×10^{10}
  (d) 1.3737×10^{46} (e) 1.4994×10^{11} (f) 1.424×10^{18}
6 Mercury, 1.93×10^2 s   Mars, 7.6×10^2 s
  Jupiter, 2.593×10^3 s   Pluto, 1.9663×10^4 s

Page 85   A bed of roses

1 (a)

Distance from peg A in metres	5	6	4	7	3	8	2	9	1
Distance from peg B in metres	5	4	6	3	7	2	8	1	9

(b)

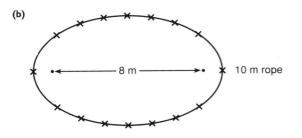

8 m   10 m rope

2 (a)

Distance from peg A in metres	5	6	4	7	3	8	2
Distance from peg B in metres	5	4	6	3	7	2	8

(b)

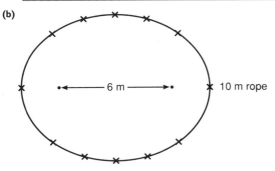

6 m   10 m rope

3 (a)

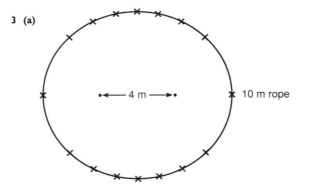

4 m   10 m rope

(b)

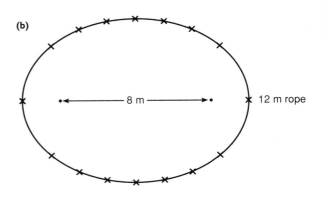

8 m   12 m rope

(c)

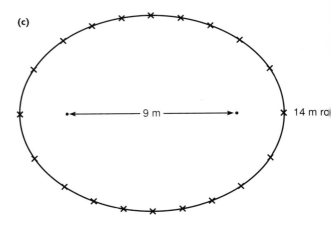

9 m   14 m rope

4 A circle.

Page 86   On the slippery slopes

1 Student's own list.
2 (a) ski jump, 1.5
     ski run, 0.5
     ramp, 0.2 (to 3dp)
     road, 0.2
     tunnel roof, 0.4
  (b) Student's comparison.
3 (a) 0.6 (b) 0.25 (c) 1.33 (to 2 dp)
  (d) 0.33 (to 2 dp) (e) 0.2 (f) 2.5

Pages 87 and 88   Life's Ups and Downs

1 EF, 4.5   GH, 0.5   IJ, 2   KL, 0.4
  MN, 2.5   OP, 1   QR, 0.75   ST, 3.5
2 2
3 (a) 2 (b) 3 (c) 1.5 (d) 5 (e) 1.5
  (f) 3.5 (g) 1.5 (h) 0.83 (i) 2 (j) 1.5
4 AB, ⁻2.5   CD, ⁻1.5   EF, ⁻0.2   GH, ⁻1,
  IJ, ⁻0.09   KL, ⁻2
5 ⁻2
6 (a) ⁻3 (b) ⁻4 (c) ⁻2 (d) ⁻1
  (e) ⁻5 (f) ⁻3.5 (g) ⁻1.5 (h) ⁻0.83
7 AB, 1.3, CD, ⁻2, EF, ⁻1, GH, 0.6, IJ, ⁻3, KL, 0.8
8 Worksheet 14, question 1
9 AB, 0.5 CD, ⁻2, EF, ⁻0.2, GH, ⁻1, IJ, 1 KL, 1.5
10 Worksheet 14, question 2
11 (a) AB, 2   CD, ⁻0.2   EF, 0.4   GH, ⁻2.5   IJ, ⁻2
     KL, ⁻0.2   MN, 2   OP, ⁻2   QR, ⁻0.25
  (b) AB and MN, IJ and OP, CD and KL

1

t	1	2	3	4
d	5	10	15	20

2 (a), (b), (c) & (d) Student's own graph

3 (a) 2, 3, $\frac{1}{2}$ 1

(b)

Equation	d = 2t	d = 3t	d = $\frac{1}{2}$t	d = t
Gradient	2	3	$\frac{1}{2}$	1

(c) The gradient has the same value as the coefficient of t.

4 (a)

x	1	2	3	4
y	3	6	9	12

Student's own graph
Gradient = 3

(b)

x	1	2	3	4
y	⁻2	⁻4	⁻6	⁻8

Student's own graph
Gradient = ⁻2

(c)

x	1	2	3	4
y	$-\frac{1}{2}$	⁻1	$-1\frac{1}{2}$	⁻2

Student's own graph
Gradient = $-\frac{1}{2}$

(d)

x	1	2	3	4
y	$\frac{1}{4}$	$\frac{1}{2}$	$\frac{3}{4}$	1

Student's own graph
Gradient = $\frac{1}{4}$

5 The gradient has the same value as the coeficient of x.

6 (a) 5   **(b)** 8   **(c)** 6   **(d)** $\frac{3}{4}$ **(e)** ⁻5   **(f)** ⁻6
(g) ⁻99   **(h)** ⁻1·5   **(i)** 14

7 (a), (b) Student's own graph
(c) 5   **(d)** f = 5t

8 (a) • Student's own graph   • 2   • f = 2t
(b) • Student's own graph   • 0·5   • f = 0·5t
(c) • Student's own graph   • 2·5   • f = 2·5t

Page 90   On the right lines

1 (a) • 2   • y = 2x   **(b)** • 1   • s = t   **(c)** • 0·5   • v = 0·5r
(d) • 0·75   • f = 0·75a   **(e)** • 3   • v = 3x   **(f)** • 0·25   • k = 0·25 m
(g) • ⁻0·5   • y = ⁻0·5x   **(h)** • ⁻1   • y = ⁻x

Page 91   Safe as houses!

1 (a)

Time in hours (s)	1	2	3	4	5
Cost in £ (C)	25	40	55	70	85

(b) Student's own graph.
(c) (0,10)

2 (a)

Time in hours (s)	1	2	3	4	5
Cost in £ (C)	28	40	52	64	76

(b) Student's own graph
(c) (0,16)

3 (a)

Time in hours (s)	1	2	3	4	5
Cost in £ (C)	36	52	68	84	100

Student's own graph
(b) (0,20)

4 (a)

Equation	C = 15t + 10	C = 12t + 16	C = 16t + 20
Point where line cuts the Cost axis	(0,10)	(0,16)	(0,20)

(b) The number at the end of the formula is the second coordinate of the point where the line cuts the Cost axis.

5 (a) Student's own answers.

Page 92   A family of lines

1 (a) Student's own graph.
(b) The lines cut the y-axis at (0,2)
All the equations end with the number 2.
2 (a) Student's own graph.
(b) Family S lines all cut the y-axis at (0,3)
Family S equations all end with the number 3.
Family T lines all cut the y-axis at (0,4).
Family T equations all end with the number 4.
Family U lines all cut the y-axis at (0,5).
Family U equations all end with the number 5.
Family V lines all cut the y-axis at (0,⁻1).
Family V equations all end with the number ⁻1.

3 (a) (0,6)   **(b)** (0,⁻2)   **(c)** (0,5)   **(d)** (0,⁻5)   **(e)** (0,4)
(f) (0,⁻6)   **(g)** (0,⁻1)   **(h)** (0,2)   **(i)** (0,⁻3)
4 (a) • ⁻3 • (0,1)   **(b)** • 2 • (0,⁻5)   **(c)** • 4 • (0,2)
(d) • 5 • (0,9)   **(e)** • 1 • (0,⁻6)   **(f)** • 7 • (0,4)
(g) • 1 • (0,⁻7)   **(h)** • 8 • (0,0)   **(i)** • 1 • (0,⁻4)
(j) • 0 • (0,2)   **(k)** • 3 • (0,0)   **(l)** • 0 • (0,7)

Page 93   Finding equations

1 (a) • 2 • (0,2) • y = 2x + 2   **(b)** • ⁻0·5 • (0,5) • y = ⁻0·5x + 5
(c) • 0·5 • (0,1) • y = 0·5x + 1   **(d)** • 3 • (0,⁻2) • y = 3x − 2
(e) • 1 • (0,⁻2) • y = x − 2   **(f)** • ⁻0·67 • (0,6) • y = ⁻0·67x + 6

Page 94   A testing time

1 Bar A Student's own graph
$l = 0·25t + 25$
Bar B Student's own graph
$l = 0·2t + 10$
2 (a) Student's own graphs.
Surface A $s = ⁻2t + 10$
Surface B $s = ⁻2·5t + 10$
(b) Surface B as the car slows down more quickly.

Pages 95 and 96   Problematic

1 b>5 where b is the weight in g
2 (a) $x^2 + 2 = 18$ **(b)** 4
3 Ramp would meet the regulations since the gradient is 0·36, which is less than 0·4
4 (a) Student's own graph
(b) If the numbers of hours is less than or equal to 20 choose Method 2.
If the numbers of hours is greater than or equal to 20 choose Method 1.
5 (a) ethene 2:1, propene 2:1
(b) ethene 1:6, propene 1:6
(c) ethene 85·7%, propene 85·7%
6 (a) • 2m/s • 2×10^{13} m/s
(b) $t = \frac{s}{v}$ **(c)** $2·6 \times 10^{⁻5}$s
7 1 892 880 guilders

8 (a) Can 302 cm^3 Carton 336 cm^3

   (b) 8·6 cm^3/p 8·3 cm^3/p

   Can is better value.

   (c) • 12   • 6

9 (a) 20   **(b)** $\frac{1}{20}$ or 0·05   **(c)** $\frac{4}{20}$ or 0·2

10 Needs 2·43 m which is less than 2·5 m, therefore has enough.

11 168 cm^2

12 Anne £187.·50, Iain £180. Anne is better paid by £7.50

13 17·5 m

Page 97   Graphic effects

1 Worksheet 15.

2 (a) Since the graph does not pass through the origin, the temperature does not vary directly as the time.

   (b) Since the graph is not a straight line, the cost does not vary directly as the weight.

   (c) Since the graph is a straight line through the origin, y varies directly as x.

Page 98   Power points

1 (a) Direct variation, graph is a straight line through the origin.

   (b) Direct variation, graph is a straight line through the origin.

   (c) Not direct variation, graph is not a straight line.

   (d) Direct variation, graph is a straight line through the origin.

   (e) Not direct variation, graph is not a straight line.

   (f) Direct variation, graph is a straight line through the origin.

   (g) Not direct variation, graph is not a straight line.

Page 99   Variation on a theme

1 (a) 5   **(b)** $V = 5R$ **(c)** • 30 volts • 50 volts • 37·5 volts

2 (a) • 3   • $V = 3R$ • 36

   (b) • 1·5   • $V = 1·5R$ • 18

   (c) • 0·5   • $V = 0·5R$ • 6

   (d) • 0·8   • $V = 0·8R$ • 9·6

3 45 newtons

4 25p

5 75·6 inches

6 7·5 ms^{-2}

7 1·6875 hours or 1 hour 41·25 min

Page 100   Mass of evidence

1 (a) Direct variation, graph is a straight line through the origin

   (b) 18 grams

   (c) 4·5

   (d) $m = 4·5\,v$

   (e) • 90 grams • 67·5 grams • 41·85 grams • 5·625 grams

2 (a) Direct variation, graph is a straight line through the origin.

   (b) 600 revolutions per minute

   (c) 30

   (d) $R = 30s$

   (e) • 1650   • 2340   • 3390

Page 101   Varying the square

1 (a) Student's own graph.

   (b) No. The graph is not a straight line.

   (c)

d^2	25	100	225	400
w	250	1000	2250	4000

   (d) Student's own graph.

   (e) Yes. The graph is a straight line through the origin.

   (f) 10

   (g) $w = 10d^2$

   (h) • 6250 grams • 25 000 grams • 100 000 grams

2 (a) Student's own graph.

   (b) No. The graph is not a straight line.

   (c)

l^2	625	1296	2401	4096	6561	10 000
t	1	1·2	1·4	1·6	1·8	2

Student's own graph.

   (d) No. The graph is not a straight line.

   (e)

$\sqrt{l}$	5	6	7	8	9	10
t	1	1·2	1·4	1·6	1·8	2

Student's own graph.

   (f) Yes. The graph is a straight line through the origin.   **(g)** 0·2

   (h) $t = 0·2\sqrt{l}$ **(i)** • 0·08   • 0·04   • 0·22

Page 102   Inverting the square

1 (a) Student's own graph. No. The graph is not a straight line.

   (b)

$\frac{1}{R}$	0·5	0·33	0·25	0·2
l	5	3·33	2·5	2

   (c) Yes. The graph is a straight line through the origin.

   (d) 10   **(e)** $l = \frac{10}{R}$ **(f)** • 1   • 0·5   • 0·2

2 (a) Student's own graph. No. The graph is not a straight line.

   (b)

$\frac{1}{d^2}$	1	0·25	0·11	0·06
l	64	16	7·11	4

   (c) Yes. The graph is a straight line through the origin.

   (d) 64   **(e)** $l = 64 \times \frac{1}{d^2}$ or $l = \frac{64}{d^2}$

Page 103   A variety of problems

1 168 cm^3

2 10·4 km

3 24 m/s

4 £62·50

5 £7·50

6 112 500 joules

Page 104   Powerful numbers

1 (a) 2^5 **(b)** 5^3 **(c)** 4^6 **(d)** r^4

   (e) t^9 **(f)** y^7 **(g)** z^{11}

2 (a) 3×3 **(b)** $2 \times 2 \times 2 \times 2 \times 2$

   (c) $4 \times 4 \times 4$ **(d)** $5 \times 5 \times 5 \times 5 \times 5 \times 5$

   (e) $t \times t \times t$ **(f)** $v \times v \times v \times v \times v \times v \times v \times v \times v \times v \times v$

   (g) $r \times r \times r \times r \times r \times r \times r \times r$ **(h)** $s \times s \times s \times s \times s \times s \times s \times s \times s \times s \times s \times s$

   (i) $5 \times 5 \times 5 \times 5 \times 5 \times 5 \times 5$ **(j)** g

   (k) $y \times y \times y \times y \times y \times y \times y \times y \times y$

   (l) $a \times a \times a \times a \times a \times a \times a \times a \times a \times a \times a \times a$

3 (a) 64   **(b)** 64   **(c)** 216   **(d)** 64

   (e) 15   **(f)** 1   **(g)** 243   **(h)** 256

   (i) 729   **(j)** 256   **(k)** 2401   **(l)** 7776

   (m) 1   **(n)** 100 000   **(o)** 1024   **(p)** 13

4 (a) 2^2 **(b)** 3^2 **(c)** 4^2

   (d) 2^3 **(e)** 5^2 **(f)** 5^3

5 (a) 16 384   **(b)** 6561   **(c)** 3125

   (d) 262 144   **(e)** 1 679 616   **(f)** 10 000 000

   (g) 39·0625   **(h)** 1·1236

6 (a) 3^6 **(b)** 2^5 **(c)** 3^7 **(d)** 4^6 **(e)** 4^8 **(f)** 5^6

7 The highest power is 26.

8 $9·2233 \times 10^{18}$

9 The number is too large to be displayed.

10 (a) The answer to each is 1.

   (b) Student's own choice.

   (c) Any number raised to the power 0 has value 1.

Pages 105 and 106   Indices rule

1. (a) 5^{10} (b) 3^9 (c) 7^9
   (d) a^{12} (e) p^{12} (f) s^{13}
2. Student's own conclusion.
3. (a) 6^8 (b) 3^{16} (c) 8^{12} (d) 9^{15}
   (e) 10^{14} (f) 7^{20} (g) u^{20} (h) t^{23}
   (i) c^{20} (j) c^{14} (k) n^{21} (l) r^{15}
4. (a) 7^{17} (b) 12^{18} (c) 17^{30} (d) 3^{20}
5. (a) $15a^7$ (b) $8c^{15}$ (c) $28t^{12}$ (d) $24d^{11}$
   (e) $15p^7$ (f) $28c^9$
6. (a) 4^2 (b) 3^3 (c) 8^1 or 8 (d) 7^2
7. Student's own conclusion.
8. (a) 5^4 (b) 9^6 (c) 7^4 (d) 6^7
   (e) 15^8 (f) 9^2 (g) v^4 (h) z^{14}
   (i) c^{13} (j) k^6 (k) b^{11} (l) r^{11}
9. (a) $12c^5$ (b) $14v^7$ (c) $15b$ (d) $32k^4$
   (e) $48f^4$ (f) $30c^2$
10. (a) $4c^8$ (b) $2v^9$ (c) $5b^4$ (d) $4k^6$ (e) $8f^{10}$ (f) $5c^6$
11. (a) $4c^5$ (b) $2v^7$ (c) $5b$ (d) $4k^4$ (e) $8f^4$
    (f) $5c^2$ (g) $5v^3$ (h) $7d^5$ (i) $7p$
12. (a) 8^6 (b) 4^6 (c) 12^8 (d) 13^3
    (e) h^{13} (f) c^2 (g) k^5 (h) p^8
13. (a) 4^{21} (b) 3^{40} (c) 8^{30} (d) d^{54}
14. Student's own conclusions.
15. (a) 6^{35} (b) 8^{40} (c) 12^{21} (d) 9^{40}
    (e) 15^{42} (f) 11^{36} (g) 18^{27} (h) 10^{32}
    (i) c^{30} (j) t^{32} (k) y^{35} (l) b^{54}
16. (a) $216h^3$ (b) $625f^4$ (c) $49k^2$ (d) $1024k^5$
    (e) $729k^6$ (f) $81r^2$ (g) $64u^6$ (h) $128f^7$
17. (a) 8^9f^9 (b) 7^6j^6 (c) $12^{17}t^{17}$ (d) 15^9j^9
    (e) 15^4f^4 (f) 23^7y^7 (g) 18^6b^6 (h) $16^{14}s^{14}$

Pages 107 and 108   The root of all power

1. (a) 4 (b) 5 (c) 8 (d) 10 (e) 2 (f) 3
   (g) 1 (h) 0 (i) 2 (j) 3 (k) 1 (l) 0
2. (a) 2·04 (b) 2·92 (c) 2·29 (d) 6·20 (e) 1·97 (f) 0·5
   (g) 0·2 (h) 1·09 (i) 3·16 (j) 1·99 (k) 4·36 (l) 1·82
3. (a) 2 cm (b) 2·29 cm (c) 4·64 cm (d) 10 cm
4. (a) 4 (b) 5 (c) 8 (d) 10
   (e) 9 (f) 7 (g) 1 (h) 0
5. (a) 1·12 (b) 2·88 (c) 2·76 (d) 8·24
   (e) 10·05 (f) 11·62 (g) 0·5 (h) 0·85
6. $a^{\frac{1}{3}} \times a^{\frac{1}{3}} \times a^{\frac{1}{3}} = a^{\frac{1}{3}+\frac{1}{3}+\frac{1}{3}} = a^1 = a$

   $a^{\frac{1}{3}}$ must be the same $\sqrt[3]{a}$

   $a^{\frac{1}{3}} = \sqrt[3]{a}$

7. $a^{\frac{1}{4}} \times a^{\frac{1}{4}} \times a^{\frac{1}{4}} = a^{\frac{1}{4}+\frac{1}{4}+\frac{1}{4}} = a^1 = a$

   $a^{\frac{1}{4}}$ must be the same $\sqrt[4]{a}$

   $a^{\frac{1}{4}} = \sqrt[4]{a}$

8. (a) 2 (b) 3 (c) 4 (d) 10 (e) 2 (f) 3
   (g) 0 (h) 1 (i) 6 (j) 5 (k) 11 (l) 1
9. (a) 1·96 (b) 3·07 (c) 2·41 (d) 7·73
   (e) 2·95 (f) 0·73 (g) 0·1 (h) 1·80
   (i) 3·75 (j) 2·25 (k) 6·05 (l) 2·06
   (m) 2 (n) 3·02 (o) 10·00 (p) 5·62
10. (a) 11·58 cm (b) 8·00 cm (c) 30·0 cm (d) 4·00 cm
    (e) 14·99 cm (f) 12·0 cm

Page 109 Detour: The times they are a-changing

1. (a) • 21×43
       10×86
       5×172
       2×344
       1×688
       $688 + 172 + 43 = 903$
   • 23×22
       11×44
       5×88
       2×176
       1×352
       $352 + 88 + 44 + 22 = 506$
   • 46×115
       23×230
       11×460
       5×920
       2×1840
       1×3680
       $3680 + 920 + 460 + 230 = 5290$
   • 32×245
       16×490
       8×980
       3×1960
       2×3920
       1×7840
       $\qquad 32 \times 245 = 7840$

   (b) Students check answers using a calculator.
2. Student report.
3. (a)

• $156 \times 642 = 100\ 152$ • $236 \times 531 = 125\ 316$

• $425 \times 63 = 26\ 775$

• $1425 \times 2476 = 3\ 528\ 300$

   (b) Students check answers using a calculator.
4. Student report.

Page 110   Bargain bars

1 **(a)** 35p   **(b)** 15p
2 **(a)** 40p   **(b)** 20p
3 Students check graph.
4 **(a)** 28p   **(b)** 21p
5 **(a)** 56p   **(b)** 32p
6 **(a)** 30p   **(b)** 54p
7 **(a)** 16p   **(b)** 4p

Page 111   A graphic illustration

1 **(a)** · £5 · £4   **(b)** · £17 · £13   **(c)** see graph for **2(c)**
2 **(a)** · £2 · £4   **(b)** · £7 · £8
(c)

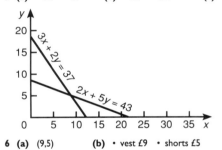

3 **(a)** (9,4)   **(b)** adult £9, child £4
4 **(a)** · £5 · £11   **(b)** · £7 · £3   **(c)** see graph for **5(c)**
5 **(a)** · £3 · £7   **(b)** · £9 · £19   **(c)**

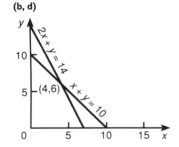

6 **(a)** (9,5)   **(b)** · vest £9 · shorts £5

Page 112   Picture the scene

1 **(a)** (0,10) (5,5) (10,0)
  (c) (0,14) (2,10) (6,2)
  (b, d)

(e) (4,6) $x = 4$ and $y = 6$
2 **(a)** (1,11) $x = 1$ and $y = 11$
  (b) (4,2) $x = 4$ and $y = 2$
  (c) (2,2) $x = 2$ and $y = 2$
  (d) (2,4) $x = 2$ and $y = 4$
  (e) (2,5) $x = 2$ and $y = 5$
  (f) (3,2) $x = 3$ and $y = 2$
3 numbers are 14 and 5
4 books cost £9 and £7
5 angles are 75° and 15°
6 potatoes weigh 25 kg or 5 kg
7 tape cost £8

Page 113   Nardoni's

1 $4c + b = 450$ $3c + b = 355$ $b = 70\ c = 95$
2 $5i + f = 335$ $3i + f = 225$ $i = 55\ f = 60$
3 **(a)** (5,1)   **(b)** (2,4)   **(c)** (4,3)   **(d)** (1,7)
  (e) (2,4)   **(f)** (7,1)   **(g)** (5,9)   **(h)** (2,1)
4 **(a)** (5,2)   **(b)** (4,1)   **(c)** (6,2)   **(d)** (2,2)
  (e) (1,4)   **(f)** (1,1)   **(g)** (8,2)   **(h)** (11,4)

Page 114   Eliminate, eliminate!

1 **(a)** (2,5)   **(b)** (5,2)   **(c)** (10,2)   **(d)** (3,3)   **(e)** (3,9)
  (f) (5,2)   **(g)** (⁻1,1)   **(h)** (3,7)   **(i)** (10,2)   **(j)** (3,9)
2 35p
3 50 cm
4 25, 38
5 85p
6 £8
7 £9·80

Pages 115   Balancing up

1 **(a)** (3,1)   **(b)** (5,⁻1)   **(c)** (1,3)   **(d)** (1,3)
  (e) (3,⁻3)   **(f)** (1,1)   **(g)** (⁻1,2)   **(h)** (⁻1,⁻1)
2 £11·50
3 £2·20
4 0·5 kg
5 **(a)** (4,2)   **(b)** (3,5)   **(c)** (2,2)   **(d)** (1,⁻1)
  (e) (2,0)   **(f)** (2,⁻1)   **(g)** (7,1)   **(h)** (3,10)
6 **(a)** (2,1)   **(b)** (5,1)   **(c)** (2,0)   **(d)** (7,3)
  (e) (7,⁻5)   **(f)** (3,2)   **(g)** (2,5)   **(h)** (1,3)

Page 116   Dilatation

1 **(a)** and **(b)** Students measure lengths.
  (c) Scale factor 2
2 **(a)** and **(b)** Students measure lengths.
  (c) Scale factor 2
3 Worksheet 16
4 **(a)** Students measure lengths.
  (b) Scale factor $\frac{1}{2}$
5 Worksheet 17
6 Students measure lengths.
7 Worksheet 18

Page 117   Triangles

1 **(a)** · PR   **(b)** · FH   **(c)** · XZ
       · PQ   · FG   · YZ
       · QR   · HG   · XY
2 **(a)** 30°   **(b)** 5·5 cm   **(c)** 7·1 cm   **(d)** 28·6°
3 **(a)** 68°   **(b)** 14·8 cm   **(c)** 56·3°   **(d)** 1·2 cm
4 **(a)** 4·9   **(b)** 52·1°

Page 118   Angles and sides

1 **(a)** 43·3°   **(b)** 3·4 cm   **(c)** 3·2 cm   **(d)** 30 cm   **(e)** 33·7°   **(f)** 3·5 cm
2 **(a)** Student's own sketch.   **(b)** 68·9°
3 8·5 m
4 $a = 18·1$ m $b = 8·7$ m $c = 7·0$ m $d = 0·7$ m
5 22·6°
6 2·2 m
7 25·6°
8 6·7 m

Page 119   Bearing up

1 Lexton 085°, Dargel 120°, Parton 225°, Semple 281°
2 **(a)** Student's own sketch.   **(b)** 24 km

3 (a) Student's own sketch. **(b)** 114 km
4 (a) • 070° • 325° • 090°
   (b) Student's own sketch. **(c)** 10·3 km
5 333°

Page 120   Poles apart

1 (a) 2·79 m **(b)** 4·39 m **(c)** 3·74 m **(d)** 4·13 m
2 (a) 14·23 m **(b)** 5·53 m **(c)** 7·69 m **(d)** 7·56 m
3 (a) 0·66 m **(b)** 0·30 m **(c)** 0·48 m **(d)** 0·38 m

Page 121   Find the distance

1 (a) 61 cm **(b)** 8·9 cm **(c)** 9·5 mm
   (d) 9·2 m **(e)** 12·1 mm **(f)** 4·5 mm
2 (a) Student's own sketch. **(b)** 2·08 m
3 86 cm
4 27 cm
5 62 cm
6 24 cm
7 (a) 2·9 m **(b)** 2·5 m

Page 122   How calculating!

1 (a) 53·1° **(b)** 27° **(c)** 47·2° **(d)** 55·8°
2 (a) 7 cm **(b)** 19·6 m **(c)** 11·4 mm **(d)** 14·4 m
3 23·4 cm
4 53°
5 20 cm
6 (a) 153 m **(b)** 147 m
7 (a) 9·1 m **(b)** 72°
8 (a) Student's own sketch. **(b)** 43·3 km **(c)** 50 km

Pages 123 and 124   Mail order

1

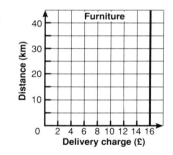

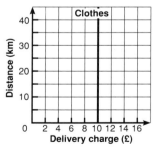

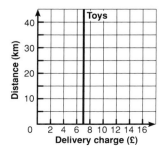

2 (a) A(3,4) B(3,2) C(3,0) D(3,⁻1)
   (b) The x-coordinates are all 3.
3 (a) Any four pairs of coordinates with the first coordinate 7.
   (b)

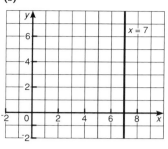

4 (a) – (f)

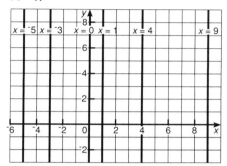

5

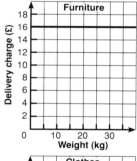

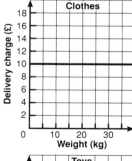

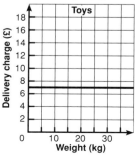

152

6 (a) A(5,3) B(2,3) C(⁻1,3) D(⁻3,3)

(b) The y-coordinates are all 3.

7 (a) Any four pairs of coordinates with the second coordinate 8.

(b)

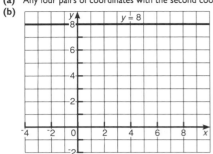

8

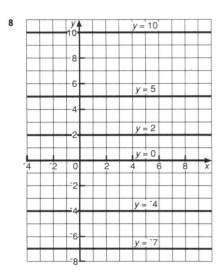

9 (a)

Weight	4 kg	2 kg	3 kg	1·5 kg
Distance	10 km	30 km	5 km	12 km
Delivery charge	No charge	£15	No charge	No charge

(b) No charge   **(c)** £15

10 (a) A(1,3) B(3,3) C(4,2) D(1,1) E(3,⁻1) F(5,⁻1)

(b) The maximum value is 5.

11 (a)

(b)

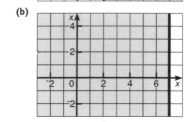

(c)

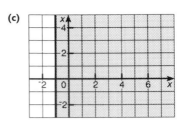

(d)

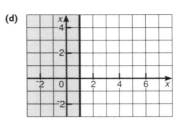

12 (a) A(⁻3,1) B(1,2) C(3,1) D(3,3) E(5,2) F(6,3)

(b) The maximum value is 3.

13 (a)

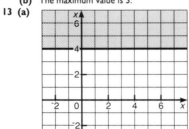

(b)

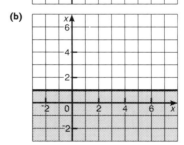

(c)

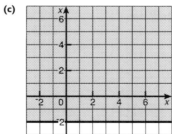

(d)

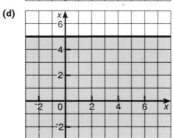

14 (a) $x \leqslant 4$ **(b)** $y \geqslant {}^{-}3$

1 (a)

Distance d	Weight w	d + 4w	Charge £
1	4	9	0
3	3	9	0
4	4	12	15
6	6	18	15
4	3	10	15
5	1	7	0
3	2	7	0
6	2	10	15

(b), (c), (d), (e) & (f)

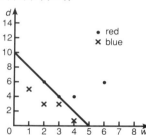

2 (a)

Distance d	Weight w	d + 4w	Charge £
1	1	5	0
2	3	14	15
1	2	9	0
6	1	10	0
3	3	15	15
7	1	11	0
5	2	13	15

(b), (c), (d), (e) & (f)

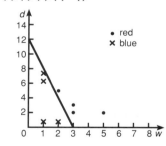

3

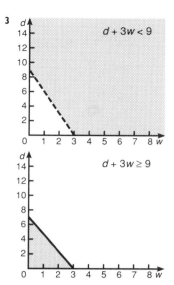

$d + 3w < 9$

$d + 3w \geq 9$

4 (a)

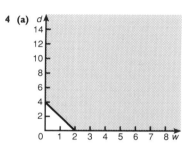

(b)

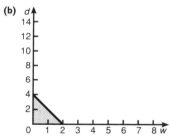

(c)

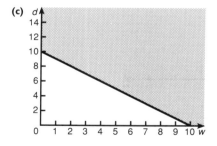

(d)

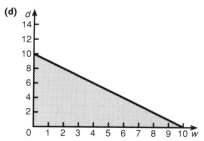

154

5 (a)

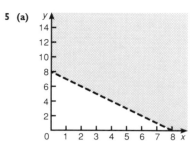

(b)

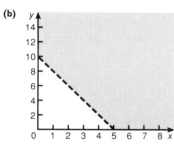

(c)

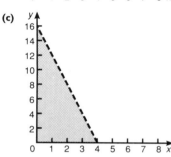

(d)

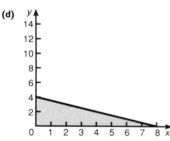

(e)

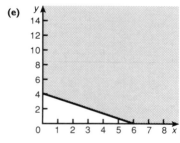

(f)

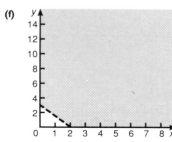

6 (a) • Transit Carriers, there would be no charge.
     • Transit Carriers, there would be no charge.
     • Blue Star, there would be no charge.
     • Either, both would charge £15

(b) If $d + 2w < 10$ and $d + 4w < 12$ use either company.
    If $d + 2w < 10$ and $d + 4w \geq 12$ use Transit Carriers.
    If $d + 2w \geq 10$ and $d + 4w < 12$ use Blue Star.
    Otherwise use either.

Pages 127 and 128   What's the problem?

1 (a) 17·7 km   **(b)** 2·8 km
2 (a) Alex £7125   William £15 625
   (b) £13 650   £9100
3 $£2^5 = £32$ and $£5^2 = £25$ so $£2^5 > £5^2$
4 (a) 11   **(b)** 40
5 (a) Student's own explanation.
   (b) 66°   **(c)** 4 m
6 Yes, since 346 cm² > 340 cm².
7 (a) 1200 miles   **(b)** 192 miles
8 97 kg
9 44 kg
10 (a)

Number of rings (R)	1	2	3	4	5	6
Number of strands (S)	0	5	10	15	20	25

   (b) 35   **(c)** $S = 5R - 5$
   (d) 80 strands   **(e)** 26 rings

Page 129   Central A Part 1

1 (a) 16·8 m²   **(b)** 17 m
2 Frank requires $9\frac{1}{10}$ m. He does not have enough since $9\frac{1}{10} > 9$
3 (a) 140 litres   **(b)** No, since 190 litres > 180 litres
4 13·188
5 (a) $4x + 12$ **(b)** $6a - 15$
6 (a) $6p + 5q$ **(b)** $13x - 6$
7 (a) 40   **(b)** 30
8 £56·40
9 636
10 (a) $h = 7$ **(b)** $x < 2$ **(c)** $m = 3$

Page 130   Central A Part 2

1 (a) • 48 • 90
   (b) • 18 min • 66 min
2 10 km
3 (a) Student's drawing.
   (b) • 110 km • 286°
4 1 day
5 (a) Student's drawing.
   (b)

Stack number (s)	1	2	3	4	5
Number of barrels (b)	6	9	12	15	18

   (c) $b = 3s + 3$ **(d)** 33
6 $a = 30$, $b = 5$ cm, $c = 7 \cdot 1$ cm, $d = 45$, $e = 60$, $f = 10$
7 (a) 2·45   **(b)** 10·8   **(c)** 7000
8 (a) 14·8 km, 15·2 cm   **(b)** 0·0545 cm, 0·0555 cm
9 11 rolls

Page 131   Central A Part 3

1 (a) ⁻3   **(b)** ⁻10   **(c)** ⁻4   **(d)** ⁻28
   (e) ⁻4   **(f)** 16   **(g)** 13   **(h)** 3
2 (a) $9x - 6$ **(b)** $5x - 2$ **(c)** $14y + 4$ **(d)** $15 - y$
3 (a) $p = ⁻8$ **(b)** $m = ⁻4$ **(c)** $r = 3$ **(d)** $a = ⁻12$
4 (a) $\frac{1}{3}$ **(b)** $\frac{4}{9}$ **(c)** $\frac{7}{9}$
5 (a) • $\frac{3}{14}$ • $\frac{16}{175}$ **(b)** 60

6 £62.75
7 (a) £100 (b) £225
8 £282·50
9 (a)

Number of days	Cost £
1	28
2	44
3	60
4	76

  (b) $c = 16d + 12$
  (c) £300
10 B
11 (a) 75·36 inches (b) 1884 inches (c) 48·3 m
12 15·5 m^2

Page 132   Central A Part 4

1 £2070
2 1846 FF
3 75 min or 1 hour 15 min
4 $a = 1·5$ cm, $b = 10·5$ cm
5 4·5 cm
6 1170 cm^2
7 mean = 8, median = 7·5, mode = 6
8 mean = 3·11, median = 3, mode = 4
9 12·3
10 (a) 6·4 cm (b) 6·3 cm
11 2·4 m
12 $AB = 10$ units

Page 133   Central B Part 1

1 (a) $12x$ (b) $6w + 9v$
2 (a) $6x + 12y$ (b) $20b - 35c$
3 (a) $18x + 20y$ (b) $20f + 30g$
4 (a) $2(4x + 3)$ (b) $3(3v - 4h + 2k)$ (c) $a(a + 5)$
  (d) $f(4f + 4g - 1)$ (e) $4t(t + 3s)$
5 (a) $x^2 + 5x + 6$ (b) $y^2 + y - 12$
  (c) $f^2 - 12f + 35$ (d) $p^2 - p - 2$
6 (a) $\frac{1}{2}$ (b) $\frac{3}{8}$ (c) $\frac{4}{15}$
7 $\frac{9}{20}$
8 (a) $\frac{5}{3}$ or $1\frac{2}{3}$ (b) $\frac{5}{6}$ (c) $\frac{9}{20}$
9 10
10 (a) 28 ml (b) 35 ml (c) 84 ml
11 117
12 (a) 168 m^3 (b) 343·2 m^2
13 (a) 280 000 mm^3 (to 2 significant figures)
  (b) 94 000 mm^2 (to 2 significant figures)
14 (a) $\frac{1}{2}$ (b) $\frac{2}{36}$ or $\frac{1}{18}$ (c) $\frac{1}{36}$
  (d) $\frac{3}{36}$ or $\frac{1}{12}$ (e) $\frac{1}{36}$ (f) $\frac{11}{36}$
15 £223·13
16 £948·75

Page 134   Central B Part 2

1 51 km/h, 108 km/h
2 42 km
3 (a) 30 min (b) 30 miles (c) 40 mph
4 (a) 41·2° (b) 4·6
5 27·6°
6 (a) 5, 3 and 8, 5
  (b) 12, 6·5 and 21, 14·5
  (c) 29·5, 25 and 34, 9
7 (a)

7 (a)

Pattern number (p)	1	2	3	4	5
Number of matches (m)	5	9	13	17	21

  (b) $m = 4p + 1$
  (c) straight line
  (d)

8 (a) (4,19) (b) (0,3) (c) (5,28) (d) ($^-$3,12)

Page 135   Central B Part 3

1 $7x + 45 = 3x + 645$ $x = 150$
  Each box of chocolates weighs 150 grams.
2 (a) $x = 5$ (b) $c = 2$ (c) $p < 6$ (d) $d < 3$
  (e) $y = 1$ (f) $x = 2$ (g) $t = 3$ (h) $p = 25$
3 (a) £7100 (b) $Y = \frac{s}{50} - 120$ (c) 24 years old
4 $l = 8$ metres
5 gradient = 0·2
6 Student's own graph. Equation is $c = 9h + 3$
7 4·8 joules
8 $5·48 \times 10^7$
9 1×10^{-9}
10 $1·8 \times 10^{10}$ metres
11 Student's scale drawing. Robbie lands 20 m downstream.

Page 136   Central B Part 4

1 (a) 9 (b) $F = 9P$ (c) 990
2 (a) No, since the graph is not a straight line through the origin.

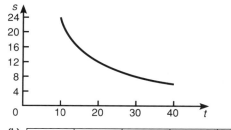

  (b)

$\frac{1}{t}$	0·1	0·05	0·033	0·025
s	24	12	8	6

  (c)

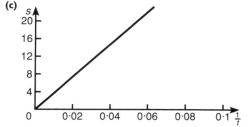

  (d) $k = 240$
  (e) • 15 • 24
3 (a) (4,2) (b) (2,6)
4 45p
5 (a) 125 (b) 32 (c) 10 000 000
  (d) 4096 (e) 1 (f) 4 (g) 0 (h) 3
6 (a) 5^{10} (b) p^5 (c) $8a^8$ (d) 7^6 (e) r^{10}
  (f) $4c^3$ (g) $64r^3$ (h) $100\,000s^5$

7 (a) Any four points of coordinates with first coordinate 5.

(b)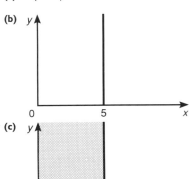

(c)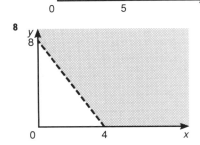

8

9 6·8 km

10 (a) 39·6 cm **(b)** 5·8 mm

Answers for worksheets

1   C(1,3,4), D(4,2,1), E(2,0,3), F(2,0,0), G(4,0,3)

2,3

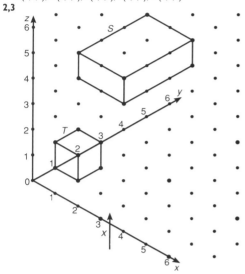

2   Prism S Cuboid
     Prism T Cube
3   Students draw triangular prism.

W2   Cylinder labels

1,2   Practical work
3   For each cylinder, the length measured on the strip is approximately the same as πd.
4

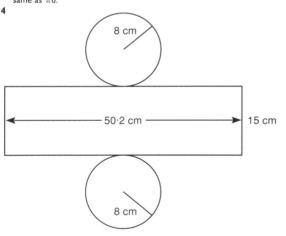

W3   Pay slips

	(a)	(b)	(c)
C Rupert	£270·50	£88·78	£181·72
R Turner	£289·24	£116·99	£172·25
E Nell	£1312·45	£412·88	£899·57
S Bank	£1422·03	£434·12	£987·91

W4   Clocking in and out

1   £216·20
2   £280·80

W5   Count the miles

1

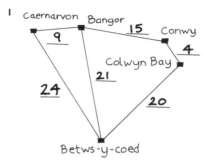

2

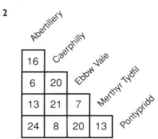

3 (a)

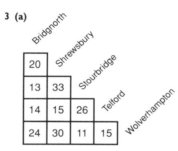

(b)

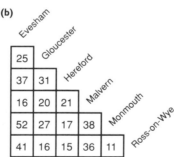

4

W6   Hexaflexgon

Students do practical work.

W7 Getting a tan

1 (a) $\tan a° = 0.375$
  (b) $\tan b° = 0.75$
  (c) $\tan c° = 2.5$
2 (a) $48.6°$ (b) $60°$ (c) $29.7°$

W8 Flying the flag

1 3.9 m
2 7.7 m
3 1.1 m
4 (a) 7.8 m (b) 2.0 m (c) 4.8 m

W9 A class act 1

Table 1

Weight	Frequency	Cumulative frequency
50	2	2
51	3	5
52	5	10
53	9	19
54	7	26
55	4	30
56	2	32
57	1	33

Curve 1

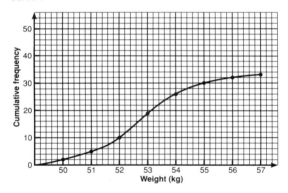

Table 2

Marks	Frequency	Cumulative frequency
1–10	3	3
11–20	4	7
21–30	6	13
31–40	10	23
41–50	5	28
51–60	2	30
61–70	1	31

Curve 2

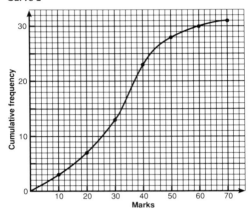

W10 A class act 2

Table 3

Marks	Tally	Frequency	Cumulative frequency
1–10	ЦНТ	5	5
11–20	ЦНТ I	6	11
21–30	ЦНТ ЦНТ	10	21
31–40	ЦНТ III	8	29
41–50	ЦНТ I	6	35

Curve 3

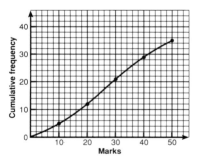

Table 4

Reaction times	Tally	Frequency	Cumulative frequency
0·6 – 1·0	ll	2	2
1·1 – 1·5	ЦНТ ЦНТ	10	12
1·6 – 2·0	ЦНТ lll	8	20
2·1 – 2·5	ЦНТ lll	8	28
2·6 – 3·0	ЦНТ	5	33
3·1 – 3·5	ll	2	35

Curve 4

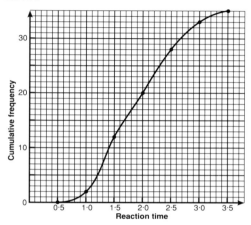

W12   Locus diagrams

Diagram 5

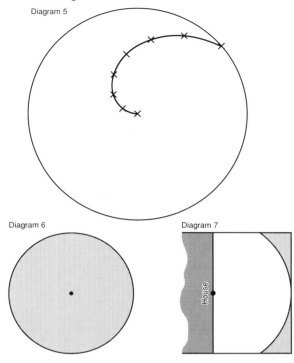

Diagram 6

Diagram 7

House

W13   Locus diagrams

Diagram 8

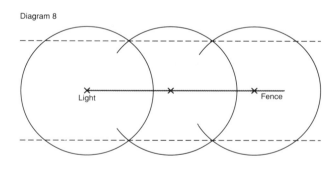

Light

Fence

W11   Locus diagrams

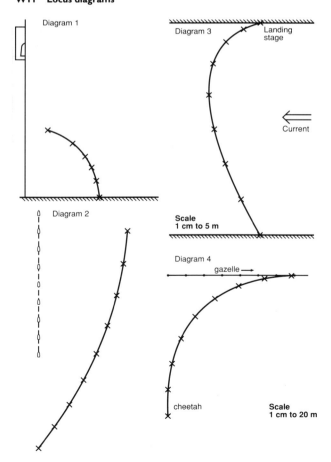

Diagram 1

Diagram 3

Landing stage

Current

Scale
1 cm to 5 m

Diagram 2

Diagram 4

gazelle →

cheetah

Scale
1 cm to 20 m

Diagram 9

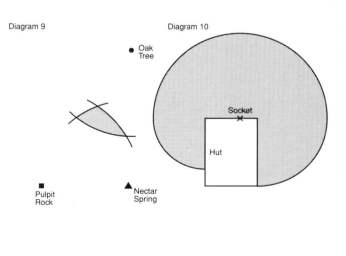

● Oak Tree

■ Pulpit Rock

▲ Nectar Spring

Diagram 10

Socket

Hut

W14   Life's ups and downs

Gradient of AB   = 8 ÷ 5
                  = 1·6
Gradient of AC   = 16 ÷ 10
                  = 1·6
Gradient of BC   = 8 ÷ 5
                  = 1·6
All gradients are the same regardless of which points are used.
Gradient of PQ   = 10 ÷ 5
                  = 2
Gradient of RS   = 14 ÷ 7
                  = 2
Gradient of TU   = 8 ÷ 4
                  = 2
Gradients are the same and lines are parallel.

W15   Graphic descriptions

1 **(a)** varies directly   **(b)** does not vary directly
   (c) does not vary directly   **(d)** varies directly
   (e) does not vary directly   **(f)** varies directly

W16   Dilatation

1

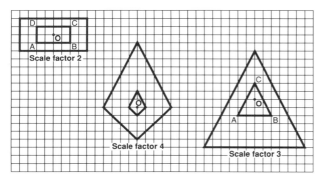

2

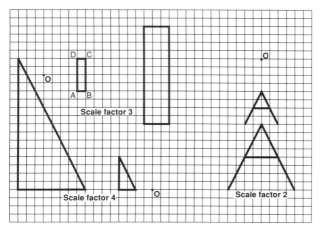

W17   More dilatation

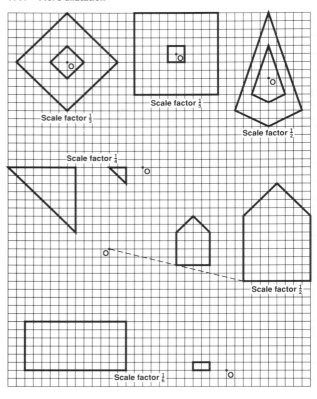

161

1

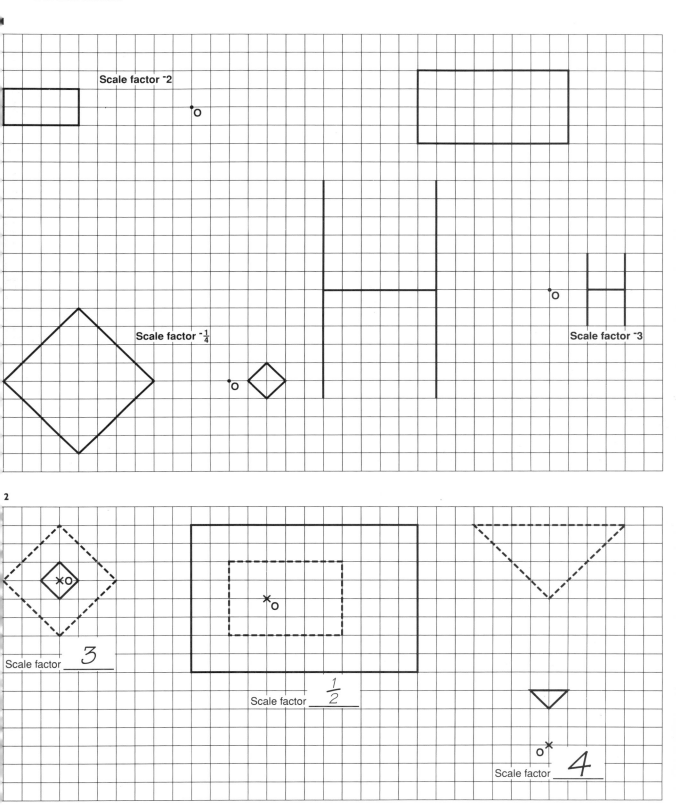

Scale factor ⁻2

Scale factor ⁻$\frac{1}{4}$

Scale factor ⁻3

2

Scale factor _____ 3

Scale factor _____ $\frac{1}{2}$

Scale factor _____ 4

Front cover: Spirals in nature. The seeds at the centre of a Sun Flower spiral out from the centre. This spiral pattern often occurs in nature and is related to a number pattern called the Fibonacci sequence.

Acknowledgements

The authors and publisher would like to thank the following for permission to reproduce photographs:

p. 11 ZEFA; p. 21 Q. A. Photos Ltd; p. 22 J. Allan Cash Ltd; p. 79 Peter Gould; p. 80 Lawrence Migdale/Science Photo Library; p. 80 CERN; p. 80 J. Allan Cash Ltd; p. 81 NASA/Science Photo Library; p. 81 David Leah/Science Photo Library; p. 83 Science Photo Library; p. 90 J. Allan Cash Ltd; p. 90 Philip Parkhouse; p. 94 Transport Research Laboratory; p. 99 Robert Harding Picture Library; p. 99 J. Allan Cash Ltd; p. 103 Robert Harding Picture Library; p. 103 Blackpool Pleasure Beach; p. 114 J. Allan Cash Ltd.

Cover image by Heather Angel.

We would also like to thank Ordnance Survey for use of Crown Copyright material on page 61.

Every effort has been made to contact copyright holders of material reproduced in this book. Any omissions will be rectified in subsequent printings if notice is given to the publisher.

Heinemann Educational,
a division of Heinemann Publishers (Oxford) Ltd
Halley Court, Jordan Hill, Oxford OX2 8EJ

OXFORD   LONDON   EDINBURGH
MADRID   ATHENS   BOLOGNA   PARIS
MELBOURNE   SYDNEY   AUCKLAND   SINGAPORE   TOKYO
IBADAN   NAIROBI   HARARE   GABORONE
PORTSMOUTH NH (USA)

ISBN 0 435 52983 8

© Scottish Secondary Mathematics Group 1995

First published 1995

95 96 97 98 99   10 9 8 7 6 5 4 3 2 1

Designed and produced by VAP Group Ltd, Kidlington, Oxford

Illustrated by Jane Bottomley and Trevor Mason

Printed in Spain by Mateu Cromo